Adventures in Greatness

Speed and Comprehension Reader

A Beka Book® Pensacola, FL 32523-9100
a ministry of PENSACOLA CHRISTIAN COLLEGE

Speed and Comprehension Readers
Adventures in Other Lands
Adventures in Nature
Adventures in Greatness

Adventures in Greatness:
Speed and Comprehension Reader
Third Edition

Staff Credits
Editors: Heidi Mayfield
Designer: Stan Shimmin
Layout Assistants: James de Leon
Illustrators: Emily Hayley, Steven Hileman, John Ball, Christy Smith, Brian Jekel, Karen Bramblet

Copyright © 2000, 1992, 1983 Pensacola Christian College
All rights reserved. Printed in U.S.A. 2002

No part of this publication may be reproduced or transmitted in any form or by any means, electronic or mechanical, including photocopy, recording, or any information storage and retrieval system, or by license from any collective or licensing body, without permission in writing from the publisher.

A Beka Book, a Christian textbook ministry of Pensacola Christian College, is designed to meet the need for Christian textbooks and teaching aids. The purpose of this publishing ministry is to help Christian schools reach children and young people for the Lord and train them in the Christian way of life.

Acknowledgments
"Can Do. Will Do. Did!" "He Used His Head," "Johnny-Jump-Up" from *Because He Came* by Margaret T. Applegarth, copyright 1954 by L. W. Smith. Adapted and printed with permission of Judson Press, 1-800-458-3766.

"Cartier the Explorer" from *Famous Canadian Stories* by George E. Tait. Used by permission, McClelland & Stewart, Inc. The Canadian Publishers.

"The Games Begin" from *Jim Thorpe: The Legend Remembered* by Rosemary K. Updyke ©1997 used by permission of the licenser, Pelican Publishing Company, Inc.

"Mr. McGuffey and His Reader" adapted and used by permission.

Stories by Elizabeth Rider Montgomery used by permission.

Slate texture on cover and pp. iii, v, vi, vii by Corbis Images; ship, birds, ship's wheel on cover, inside cover, title page by Corel.

Cataloging Data
    Adventures in greatness: speed and comprehension reader. — 3rd ed.
A Beka Book reading program.
vi, —p.: ill.; 23 cm.
1. Readers (Elementary). II A Beka Book, Inc.
Library of Congress: PE1119 .A28 2000
Dewey System: 428.6

To Parents and Teacher

Adventures in Greatness is a speed and comprehension reader. Although correlated with the *A Beka Book* Language Arts 6 Curriculum, the book is suitable for use in grades 6–7.

Beginning in fourth grade, the *A Beka Book* reading program provides specific opportunities for students to develop their comprehension skills. At this level, students have become personally responsible for much more history and science material and outside reading. Their vocabulary work is increased and they are expected to retain many more facts. Now is the time to begin stressing the importance of reading for information at the best possible speed. Because the reading program for the lower elementary grades stresses phonics and reading mastery, students are now ready to begin working on these other reading skills.

The best way to help students develop these skills is to provide for much practice and to provide them with a variety of stimulating, well-written reading materials. The ability to comprehend is really the ability to *concentrate*. Teach your students good habits that will help them to concentrate.

It is not helpful to turn the development of comprehension skills into a "science" by spending the reading class finding core parts of the sentence, analyzing patterns of paragraph organization, recognizing related thought groups, etc. This is unnecessary if you have the right kind of language arts program. Spend the reading class reading!

Procedure for Using *Adventures in Greatness*

The speed and comprehension exercises for grades 4–6 are purposely varied as to content, degree of difficulty, and length. They are challenging and interesting. Quizzes are included for each reading exercise.

1. Remove all quizzes and the Quiz Answer Key (pp. 147–148) from each book (or have students remove the quiz each week before beginning to read). Collate the quizzes, putting together the quizzes for each story. Quizzes will then be ready for distribution each week.
2. Make cards for the numbers 1–8 to show the amount of time that has

passed. Each card should have one large number written on it.
3. Pass out *Adventures in Greatness* and the appropriate quiz. Have students place the quiz face down on their desks. Announce the page number. Instruct students to find page announced, close their book (keeping their finger at the page), and hold the book above their head. When the class is ready, give the start signal.
4. As students are reading, time them with a watch or clock that is digital or has a second hand. Hold up a card with "1" on it after one minute has passed, "2" after two minutes have passed, etc. (or write the number quietly on the chalkboard). When students have finished reading, they should close their book, set it aside, and begin taking the quiz. No student should reopen his book after reading the quiz selection. For the first several weeks, allow time for students to read at the rate of approximately 125 words per minute. (For example, allow 7 minutes for a selection of 875 words.) As the year progresses, gradually shorten the time you allow them to read the selection. Most students should average *at least* 200 words per minute by the end of the year.
5. As they begin the quiz, they should check the number on the card you are holding and write that number at the bottom of the quiz. When all students have finished the quiz, have them exchange papers, and grade them in class. Each question has a 10 point value. Subtract from 100 the total number of points missed to get the grade. Have students record their reading time in space provided at bottom of quiz. They can then divide the number of words read by the number of minutes it took them to read to figure words per minute. (You may need to talk through the process after first few quizzes.)
6. Have students call out grades and words per minute for you to record in grade book (Example: 90/200). Then have students pass in quizzes and *Adventures in Greatness*. Follow this procedure for all Speed and Comprehension quizzes.

To the Student

We often wonder about the beginnings of things. God has told us how the world began; so we don't need to wonder about that—but what about other things? How did great men start out? How did great books and stories come into being?

These selections will take us back to the beginning, to tell us about people who began great things. You will read how some scientists got started, how some missionaries got started, how "The Legend of Sleepy Hollow" and other famous stories and books were written, and even what happened when one boy in a lumber camp began reading the Bible.

All sorts of exciting things have been begun and finished by people who thought that they could not do such enormous jobs, but then they found that with God's help they could.

As you read about these and other adventures, you might find you would like to do something great someday, too.

Contents

Rocket Man: Wernher von Braun 1
Francis Scott Key's Banner 3
Mr. McGuffey and His Readers 5
"Keep Cool with Cal" 7
Isaac Newton: "The Great Ocean of Truth" 9

Man's Beginning 11
Dr. Livingstone, I Presume? 13
Mary Slessor: Queen of the Cannibals 15
Fact or Fiction? Aesop's Fables 17
Accidental Author, *Part 1* 19
Accidental Author, *Part 2* 21

The Book That Converted Its Author, *Part 1* 23
The Book That Converted Its Author, *Part 2* 25
Momentous Decision, *Part 1* 28
Momentous Decision, *Part 2* 30

He Used His Head, *Part 1* 32
He Used His Head, *Part 2* 34
He Used His Head, *Part 3* 36
Parable of Patriotism, *Part 1* 38
Parable of Patriotism, *Part 2* 41

Inseparable Brothers, *Part 1* 44
Inseparable Brothers, *Part 2* 46
Johnny-Jump-Up, *Part 1* 49
Johnny-Jump-Up, *Part 2* 52
The Games Begin! 55

Can Do. Will Do. Did!, *Part 1* 59
Can Do. Will Do. Did!, *Part 2* 62
Can Do. Will Do. Did!, *Part 3* 65
Chappie James: Patriot of the Skies 68
The Man with Two Lives 72
Cartier the Explorer. 76

Pronunciation Key

Symbol	Example	Symbol	Example
ā	āte	ô	côrd, taught, saw
â	dâre	ŏ	nŏt
ă	făt	oi	boil
ä	fäther	o͞o	bro͞od
ə	ago (ə·gō′)	o͝o	bo͝ok
ch	chin	ou	out
ē	ēven	sh	shark
ĕ	ĕgg	th	thin
*ê (ər)	pondêr	th	there
g	good	*tṷ (cho͞o)	virtṷe
ī	īce	ū	ūnit
ĭ	ĭt	û	ûrn
j	jog	ŭ	ŭp
ks	perplex (ks = x)	zh	azure (zh = z)
kw	quart (kw = qu)	′	little (lĭt′′l; shows that the vowel is not sounded)
ng	song		
ō	ōver		

*Note: For simplicity, the alternate symbols are used for êr and tṷ.

Rocket Man: Wernher von Braun

Dewitt Steele

Until his death in 1977, Wernher von Braun was generally considered to be the most knowledgeable astronautic engineer in the world. *(Astronautics is the science dealing with space travel.)* Even as a boy Wernher was very interested in rockets. He learned as much about them as he could and soon he was making and firing them. One day he wondered whether or not his rockets could push his coaster wagon. Since he was an adventuresome lad, he decided to find out.

A short while later he fastened a number of rockets onto the sides and back of his wagon. Then he lit all the rockets. But before he could manage to climb aboard,

his wagon shot off down a crowded street. As the thrust, or push, from the rockets made the wagon go faster and faster, Wernher dashed along behind it, down the main street of the small German town where he lived. Smoke and flame came shooting out behind the wagon. People scampered out of the way. All the town was excited.

Finally his rockets burned out and his wagon rolled to a stop. After a stern lecture from the police and a warning not to do such a foolish stunt again, Wernher was sent home with his parents.

Wernher von Braun's career as a space scientist was brilliant and very successful. But it could have ended in infamy. At twenty, he was appointed chief of Adolf Hitler's army rocket corps. He developed the rockets which bombarded London in World War II. Fortunately for all involved, only a few rockets were successfully launched before the war ended.

His study of the universe led him to say shortly after the war, ". . . the more we study space, the more convinced I am of God's controlling order in a seemingly endless universe."

At the end of the war, he was invited to come to America. He did, and in 1955 became a naturalized citizen. Von Braun was in charge of the United States' space program almost from its beginning. Because of his leadership, the United States has the distinction of being the world's leader in space exploration.

 350 words

Francis Scott Key's Banner

Phyllis Rand

Every year thousands of tourists thrill to see the old, battle-scarred American flag which covers the wall of the Museum of History and Technology in Washington, D.C. It is 50 feet long and has 15 stars and 15 stripes.

This flag is the very one that inspired the lawyer Francis Scott Key while watching a fierce battle between the Americans and the British during the War of 1812. In a surprise attack, British warships had bombarded Fort McHenry, near Baltimore, Maryland, for one whole day and almost all night. Held prisoner on a British ship, Francis Scott Key could not tell who was winning the battle—only that it was violent. The next morning, by the dawn's early light, Key paced up and down the deck of the British ship and peered through the smoke and haze trying to see Fort McHenry. It was about 7 o'clock that

September morning when the mist broke and he saw the star-spangled banner still waving over the fort. In his gratitude and joy, Key rapidly penned the words that would one day be the national anthem of his country.

The next day, after Key's release, the words were printed on handbills and distributed throughout Baltimore. A few days later, the song was first sung in public. It was put to the tune of a military march of the 1700s. It became popular immediately and was played three months later at the Battle of New Orleans. The army and navy adopted the anthem, but it was not until 1931 that the song became our official national anthem by an act of Congress.

This was not the only poem written by Francis Scott Key; he wrote sonnets and hymns as well. His hymn, "Lord, With Glowing Heart I'd Praise Thee," may be found in some of our hymnals today. He was instrumental in founding the American Sunday School Union and served as its vice president for eighteen years.

Francis Scott Key died at the age of 64 on January 11, 1843, and the original Fort McHenry flag was displayed at the memorial service. Today a flag waves over his grave twenty-four hours a day.

 365 words

Mr. McGuffey and His Reader
Raymond Schuessler
(adapted)

In the early 1800s, the American Midwest was being born. Lured by the promise of plentiful land, settlers from Europe and the colonies were streaming into Ohio and the wilderness that lay beyond.

At the same time, a new concern was being voiced. How shall the children in this new frontier be educated? The people well knew the frightening truth: Mass ignorance is but a step from savagery.

Fortunately for Americans, a balding, bespectacled minister named William Holmes McGuffey stepped forward with the answer. Books! We must give the children good textbooks which will teach them how to read and how to live. His readers, first published in 1836, rolled across America like a prairie fire. Sales eventually hit 122 million, and they are still being printed today. Only the Bible has done better. Soon the readers were making their way to California mining camps and the far-away islands of the Philippines. Even the Japanese translated them.

It is impossible to calculate the religious, moral, and ethical influence that McGuffey's six readers had in shaping the American mind. Mr. McGuffey gathered or wrote stories and poems that taught children to love and respect God and their country. He taught them to love hard work and to be thrifty and honest. Millions of boys and girls read stories about obedience and self-denial, laziness, and pride.

William Holmes McGuffey was born in Washington County, Pennsylvania, on September 13, 1800. He was the oldest of Alexander and Anna McGuffey's 11 children.

McGuffey, who would become one of the leading intellectuals of the West, had little formal schooling during his early years. His mother taught him at home and had him memorize many pieces of literature. When he was 13, he passed an examination and started to teach farm children. When he was 21, he could recite whole books of the Bible.

McGuffey later graduated from college and became a professor. His best training, he said, was his country preaching. It was in church that he learned to put his ideas into simple words that everyone could understand.

It is said of McGuffey that "he taught millions how and what to read and study. He taught generations of boys and girls the joy of labor—whether manual or mental."

 370 words

"Keep Cool with Cal"

Phyllis Rand

Calvin Coolidge was America's 30th President. As Vice President under President Harding, he became the President in 1923 after President Harding became ill and died.

Vice President Coolidge was in Vermont visiting his father when he learned of President Harding's death. He was awakened by a phone call in the middle of the night telling him that he was now the President of the United States. Coolidge got up from his bed, got dressed, and then knelt to pray. Later, downstairs, his father administered the oath of office by the light of a kerosene lamp.

In 1924, Americans elected Mr. Coolidge for a full four-year term. They had come to respect him because he was a good, wise leader who used his common sense. "Keep cool with Cal," they said. Some people called him "Silent Cal" because he never wasted words; he said only what needed to be said. On one occasion, a lady told him that she had bet that she could get more than two words out of him. "You lose," he said.

Coolidge was known for his sense of humor. When asked how many people worked at the White House, he replied, "Oh, I'd say about half of them."

In his autobiography, Calvin Coolidge relates that he learned his successful political ideas from his philosophy professor at Amherst College. This professor taught his students to always follow truth wherever it might lead. He taught them that the reins of government belong in the hands of the people and that people are equal and free because God made them in His image.

Calvin learned these truths well, and in a speech given before college students in 1923, he passed on what he had learned. He said, "We do not need more material development, we need more spiritual development. We do not need more intellectual power, we need more moral power. We do not need more knowledge, we need more character. We do not need more government, we need more culture. We do not need more laws, we need more religion."

Calvin Coolidge was a very popular President, and Americans were sorry when he announced, "I do not choose to run for President in 1928." As usual, his announcement was brief and to the point.

 380 words

Isaac Newton: "The Great Ocean of Truth"

Dewitt Steele

Isaac Newton, who became one of the greatest scientists of all time, was born on Christmas Day in 1642. As an English schoolboy young Isaac enjoyed making such mechanical devices as a water clock, a stone sundial, and a small-scale windmill that could actually grind grain. Isaac enjoyed learning about and experimenting with chemicals. Although he tried as a youth of fourteen to manage the farm of his twice-widowed mother, most of Isaac's time was spent reading, solving mathematical problems, conducting experiments, and writing his observations in a notebook. His mother realized that Isaac would never be successful as a farmer, because he was too preoccupied with science. She decided that he should return to school.

When he was twenty-three years old and a college professor, he formulated the laws of gravity, developed the branch

of mathematics known as calculus, and invented the reflecting telescope. He was the first to discover that the white light of the sun is really a mixture of all seven colors of the visible light spectrum.

He always expressed humility and gratitude when he was praised. "If I have seen further, it is by standing on the shoulders of giants," he once explained.

Isaac Newton's interest in science seems to be a result of his personal curiosity about God's universe. The purpose of all his scientific study was to know and understand God better. As a Christian, Newton saw nature as God's handiwork and believed that God revealed Himself in His work as well as in His Word. As a scientist, Newton approached God's work with reverence and awe. He also studied the Bible extensively. The Bible was the basis for his faith and provided the guiding principles of his life.

Isaac Newton, eminent Christian man of science, shy bachelor, and modest private person, received the two highest honors his country could bestow. He was knighted by Queen Anne; and when he died at the age of eighty-four, he was buried in Westminster Abbey. In spite of his great success, Sir Isaac Newton stated shortly before his death: "I do not know what I may appear to the world, but to myself I seem to have been only like a boy playing on the seashore, and diverting myself in now and then finding a smoother pebble or a prettier shell than ordinary, whilst the great ocean of truth lay all undiscovered before me."

 390 words

Man's Beginning

Laurel Hicks

Evolutionists teach that man is a product of evolution, the false idea that man began as an animal and slowly changed (evolved) into man. They scoff at the truth that God created the earth and man. But the more man tries to disprove the Bible, the more proof he finds that the Bible is true. The Bible gives us the only true and reasonable record of where we came from and what our first ancestors were like.

Some people who do not choose to believe the Bible say that the first men were monkeylike creatures who gradually developed the ability to stand upright, think, talk, choose between right and wrong, and use tools. Evolutionists often argue among themselves about their ideas, because each of them has a different story of what early man was "really" like. *There is no scientific evidence that man evolved from animals, and all the evidence we have shows that the idea of evolution is not true.*

Perhaps you have seen drawings in books of hairy half-man, half-ape creatures standing around a fire, hunting for food, caring for their young, or eating berries and raw flesh. The caption on the picture may have said that this is what early man looked like. There is no evidence at all that the first men were hairy "ape men" and that after many centuries they gradually lost their hair and started to wear clothes. These pictures come from the imaginations of men who do not wish to believe the Bible. Some people have found fossil bones of what they thought were "ape men," but these were later found to be hoaxes or mistakes.

The Bible says that as soon as Adam and Eve sinned they recognized their need for clothing and made themselves clothes from fig leaves (Genesis 3:7). God knew that this was not good enough, and so He made them clothes of animal skins (Genesis 3:21).

Adam and Eve did not look like apes. Adam at his creation was undoubtedly the most handsome man who has ever lived, and Eve the most beautiful woman, for they were the direct product of God's handiwork. Our first ancestors were not apelike creatures. They were highly intelligent human beings created in the image of God.

It is true that there have been many groups of people in history who have lived in caves. Some people even today live in caves. Adam and Eve could have lived in a cave after they were sent out of the garden.

Explorers have found caves in many parts of the world that have been inhabited by people. Some of these caves are decorated with skillfully drawn pictures. No apelike creature could have done such artwork. The caves also carry evidence that their inhabitants believed in life after death. Yes, men have lived in caves. But that does not mean they were "ape men."

 475 words

Dr. Livingstone, I Presume?

Laurel Hicks

One time when Robert Moffat, the great pioneer missionary to Africa, was in England for a rest, he met a young Scottish medical doctor named David Livingstone. "Do you think I could be of help in Africa?" Livingstone asked.

"Yes," replied Moffat, "but don't come to a place where missionaries already work. From where I live and work in Africa, I can see the smoke of a thousand villages where the name of Christ has never been heard."

Doctor Livingstone went to join the Moffats in Africa. Later, he married their daughter, Mary. Then he began to travel north, far into the interior. His goal was to explore the land as he preached the gospel in order to open up the interior for other missionaries. He accomplished the task so well that he is known as the greatest of all African explorers and one of the most famous explorers in history.

David Livingstone traced the course of the Zambezi River, which he called "God's highway to the interior." He became a trusted friend of many African people, some of whom told him about the mysterious "smoke that thunders." When they led him to the "smoke," Livingstone became the first European to see Africa's largest waterfall, Victoria Falls, which he named for Queen Victoria. As the water of Victoria Falls crashes 360 feet into the Zambezi River, it makes a thunderous noise, and huge columns of mist rise 3,000 feet into the air like great clouds of smoke.

Dr. Livingstone's explorations of Africa made him one of the most famous people in the world of his day. People in England, Scotland, America, and other places eagerly followed the news of his explorations as he pushed deeper and deeper into the dark continent. Suddenly the news stopped. David Livingstone was lost! This was such an important news event that an American newspaper sent the young reporter Henry Stanley to search for him.

After searching for months, Stanley came upon a village where Livingstone, who was very ill, was resting. He greeted the great missionary with words that have become famous: "Dr. Livingstone, I presume?" Stanley explored parts of the continent with Livingstone, and later he followed his footsteps as a missionary explorer in Africa.

Dr. David Livingstone won the hearts of the Africans by his desire to share the gospel with them, his willingness to teach them new ways of growing crops and building homes, and his resolve to introduce commerce into Africa in order to destroy the slave trade. He cheerfully submitted to many dangers in order to help the people.

One morning, after he had been in Africa for about thirty years, the Africans found him dead. He had died while kneeling beside his bed in prayer. The Africans wanted to keep the memory of this great man in their land, so they buried his heart in a jungle clearing. Then they sent his body to London to be buried in Westminster Abbey, where the most famous people of Britain are honored.

 510 words

Mary Slessor: Queen of the Cannibals

Donna Covey

"Run, Ma, Run!" The cry rang through the village. It was a familiar sound to Mary Slessor, who was called the "White Ma" by the natives. She was needed again in a trouble spot. When Mary arrived, several tribes were ready to begin war. Angry shouts filled the air. Mary walked calmly into their midst and commanded them to sit down. They formed a circle around her and she sat knitting as each tribe told its side of the disagreement. With God-given courage and wisdom, Mary handed down her judgment and peacefully settled the argument. The natives had learned to respect this little red-haired missionary lady for her boldness, bravery, and wisdom.

Mary Slessor had been well prepared for her hard life as a missionary to Africa. Born in the slums of a town in Scotland in 1848, she was often mistreated by her father, who spent most of his money on liquor and frequently came home in a drunken rage. Mary had to go to work when she was eleven years old to support the family. She worked six hours, went to school six hours, and also helped at home. Her dreary life might have been unbearable had Mary not come to know Christ when she was young.

One day Mary heard about the missionary work in the rain forests of Africa's west coast, where Nigeria is today. In 1876, she sailed for Africa.

Mary Slessor went into the interior of Nigeria, a place where white people had never

15

been. There she saw a way of life that made her heart sick. The men did not work but hunted for a living; with their free time they quarreled and made war. Whenever anyone died, many servants and relatives were killed so that the dead man would not have to be alone in his "new life." Twin babies were thought to be a sign of evil; thus they were killed. The witch doctors used many evil and cruel practices. Some of the people were cannibals. Mary longed to tell these people of Christ, Who could give them real "new life" after death and help them to live a new life here on earth as well.

Mary began taking in the twins and raising them herself. With God-given bravery she would meet savage warriors and command them to go home and not fight. Strangely enough, they listened to her. Often she built houses and churches with her own hands. Mary's hard work put the natives to shame. She taught them by her example as well as by her teachings how to work hard. Many native people accepted Christ, and whole villages were changed through the power of the gospel. People for miles around came to her for advice. Slowly, many of the evil practices ceased, and Mary again moved farther into the interior to contact another savage tribe with the gospel.

During her forty years in Africa, Mary Slessor reared fifty-one African children, most of whom became pastors, teachers, or government officials. She brought Christ to thousands who had never heard of Him. She had the sale of liquor restricted, and she brought peace to a wild land. She taught the people to read, to work, to discuss their problems instead of fighting over them, and to respect human life. How could one little Scottish woman bring such change to a savage land? Only through the power of God and a life yielded to Him.

 575 words

Fact or Fiction? Aesop's Fables

Elizabeth Rider Montgomery

Note these words:
Aesop: ē′səp
Phrygian: frĭj′ē·ən; *ancient country in Asia Minor*
repellently: *repulsively*
grotesque: *ugly*
languished: *became weak or dull*
tyrant: *a cruel ruler*
tactless: *rude*
unprepossessing: *not making a good impression, unattractive*

"Don't count your chickens before they hatch." "He cried wolf once too often." "Don't kill the goose that lays the golden eggs."

You have heard remarks like these often, and undoubtedly you understand their meaning. You may even realize that when you use phrases like "sour grapes" and "lion's share" you are quoting Aesop. But did you know that Aesop did not originate all the fables which are ascribed to him? Many of the stories which we call "Aesop's Fables" existed long before Aesop's time. In fact, some scholars doubt that there ever was an Aesop. However, on the basis of what is commonly accepted as fact about this legendary person, he may have told his fables something like this.

In the sixth century before Christ, Aesop, the Phyrgian, was a slave in the household of Iadmon of Samos, an island in the Aegean Sea. Born a slave and repellently ugly, it seemed as if he had nothing but sorrow to look forward to. But what Aesop lacked in appearance he made up for in wit. By the time he reached mature manhood he had earned a reputation as a clever talker. He had an answer for every question, and a story for every occasion.

His master, Iadmon, formed the habit of depending on Aesop for much of the entertainment at the numerous banquets he gave. When the meal was under way he would send for Aesop and the slave would enter the magnificent banquet room quietly. Guests who had never seen him before might wonder at first what this grotesque slave was doing in that highborn and wealthy assemblage. But

17

they would soon forget him as tempting dishes were passed.

If conversation languished, Iadmon might ask Aesop a question, sure that the answer could be depended on to cause laughter. But more often Aesop took his cue from the talk that went on around the room. Perhaps the guests were discussing a certain tyrant's actions in meting out what seemed like undeserved punishment to some of his subjects.

Aesop would catch his master's eye, and Iadmon would ask, "What do you say to that, Aesop? What reason do you think he can have had for his action?"

Then Aesop would launch into the fable of "The Wolf and the Lamb," and the guests, listening, would forget his unprepossessing appearance as they listened to his wisdom.

"Any excuse will serve a tyrant," Aesop would finish with a bow.

And the banqueters would laugh at the story, realizing that the ugly slave had probably analyzed the situation correctly.

Or perhaps some tactless guest, familiar with Aesop's wit, might ask him if he did not often wish he were not so hideous.

"With your clever tongue, you could go far, if only your frightful face did not repel people."

Aesop would answer quietly, "A peacock once placed a petition . . ." And he would go on with the fable of "The Peacock and Juno." His concluding words, "one cannot be first in everything," would effectively silence the questioner.

Through the years Aesop gathered, adapted, or invented fables to fit every occasion. Eventually his fame spread throughout the country, and later through the civilized world. It is said that his master gave him his freedom as a reward for his wit and wisdom, so that although he could not change his ugly face, he at least changed his station in life by the use of his brain.

So runs the legend of Aesop.

 590 words

Accidental Author

Elizabeth Rider Montgomery

Part 1

Uncle Remus is a famous character in American literature. His African-American folk tales, told to "the little boy" in picturesque dialect, are known the world over. Br'er Rabbit, the little scheming, clever hero, who gets the best of the bigger animals is a favorite with children everywhere. And Uncle Remus himself is as kindly, humorous, and lovable an old man as any author has produced.

Yet the creator of Uncle Remus always insisted that he wasn't an author at all. All he did, he said, was to write down the stories he had heard all his life. And it was pure accident that he became a writer.

In 1876 Joel Chandler Harris moved with his family from Savannah, Georgia, to Atlanta, because of his children's health. Since he had worked on newspapers since the time he was fourteen, naturally a newspaper job was what he wanted to find in Atlanta.

But the job found him, instead. Captain Howell, the new publisher of the *Atlanta Constitution,* came to Harris and offered him a job as editorial paragrapher. So once again Joel Chandler Harris was working on a newspaper.

One day after Harris had been with the *Constitution* about two years, Captain Howell, the publisher, came to the desk where the small, shy Harris sat at work.

"Joe, you know that column we've been running about Uncle Si?" he said.

"Yes, sir," nodded Harris. "I've read it."

"Well, the fellow who wrote it has quit," said Captain Howell. "Would you take it on, Joe? It has quite an audience."

19

Harris hesitated. The column wasn't his type of writing at all. "I don't rightly know," he said at last. "I couldn't do it like Small did it."

"But we need a column of that type," insisted Howell. "It's popular with readers."

"Well," said Harris. "I couldn't do an Uncle Si column, but I'll do something in a different line."

"What sort of line?" asked the publisher.

Harris scratched his red head. "I don't rightly know at the moment. But I'll think of something. I'll let you know."

When he got home that night, Joel Chandler Harris tried to think what he could write. He had written editorials, columns, verse—many things during his years of newspaper work—but never a column such as Captain Howell wanted.

As his children played on the floor beside him and climbed over his chair, Harris's mind went back to his first years on a newspaper. It had been a small paper, published in a little house on the plantation of Mr. J. A. Turner. How well Harris remembered those years! A boy of fourteen when he went there, he had loved to roam the plantation after work hours with Joe Syd Turner, his employer's son. The boys had especially loved to sit in the evening on the doorstep of a cabin in the slave quarters and listen to the slaves singing and telling folk tales.

One old black man in particular was an excellent storyteller. Uncle George, they called him. He seemed to know all the lore, the songs, the superstitions, and the traditions of his race. And he was always willing to repeat them for the entertainment of the two white boys. What a rich voice Uncle George had had! Joel Harris could almost hear it now, above the noise of the romping children, singing a spiritual. . . .

Suddenly Harris sat up straight. That's what his column would be! Songs and sayings of the black people. He would begin with that old spiritual of Uncle George's: "Oh, whar shill we go w'en de great day comes. . . ."

(to be continued)

 600 words

20

Accidental Author

Elizabeth Rider Montgomery

Part 2

When Joel Chandler Harris was asked to write a newspaper column, he remembered the wonderful folk tales and songs he had learned from an old black man called Uncle George.

So Joel Chandler Harris began the column which was to lead him to fame. At first it was merely songs and poems in black dialect. But soon an old black character crept in, a former slave, whom Harris called "Uncle Remus."

Soon after Uncle Remus joined his column, Harris happened to read in *Lippincott's Magazine* an article about the folklore of the Southern blacks. The article described a few of the stories which Harris had heard many times, but without dialect the stories lacked effectiveness. How much better they were as the black people themselves told them!

Before long Harris used one of these old folk tales in his column, as told by Uncle Remus in his picturesque dialect to a little boy. The story made such a hit that soon

21

Harris was writing the old tales as a regular thing. In a short time Uncle Remus and his tales were being talked about and quoted all over Georgia.

And then, a year or so later, the fame of Uncle Remus spread beyond his native state.

Mr. J. C. Derby, representative of the New York publishing firm of A. Appleton and Company, came to see Harris.

"Have you ever thought, Mr. Harris," inquired the publishing representative, "of making a book about your Uncle Remus?"

Harris laughed. "Land, no!" he answered. "I don't write books. I just work on a newspaper."

"Well, I think you could collect your stories into a book that would sell."

"It's nice of you to say so," laughed Harris, "but people wouldn't buy a book like that."

But Mr. Derby talked fast and persuasively. At last Harris agreed to try it. Together they went through the files of the *Atlanta Consti-* *tution* which had carried the original stories. They picked out enough for a small book. In due time it was published. And to the undying amazement of Joel Chandler Harris, it was successful!

So popular, in fact, was the first volume, *Uncle Remus, His Songs and His Sayings,* that eventually Harris wrote four more books about Uncle Remus and his animal stories. When he ran out of the Negro folk tales he had heard as a boy, it became necessary to collect more. This proved to be quite a task. He had to travel all over the South, talking to people.

It may have been an accident, as Joel Chandler Harris always insisted, that he started work on a newspaper in the first place, an accident that he began writing a column about Uncle Remus, and an accident that the stories were made into a book. But it was certainly no accident that Uncle Remus became popular all over the world, and has continued popular to this day.

 465 words

The Book That Converted Its Author

Elizabeth Rider Montgomery

Part 1

Note these words:
- **theology:** *the study of God and His relation to the world*
- **mulled:** *pondered*

The balconies are crowded. Every eye is on the chariots in the great arena below as they speed faster and faster around the course. Will Ben-Hur win? Or will Messala triumph? People are shouting, screaming as the beautiful horses dash into the final stretch. But what has happened? A chariot is overturning. A driver is being dragged along the course! Surely he will be killed!

What a thrilling scene the chariot race in *Ben-Hur* is! In fact, the entire book is an exciting, absorbing story of life in the time of Christ. Though Ben-Hur is the hero, the figure of Christ is always in the background, never forgotten.

Yet *Ben-Hur: A Tale of the Christ* was not written by a religious man. The author, Lew Wallace, had been a soldier, a lawyer, a governor. When he began his famous book, he did not know what he believed about religion. He did not even know whether he believed in Christ. In fact, he began writing the book in an effort to learn for himself the truth about Jesus of Nazareth.

After his active years of service through the Civil War, General Lew Wallace returned to private life and his law practice in Crawfordsville, Indiana. For some time he was restless—the natural reaction from the excitement of war. But at last he settled down to an uneventful life.

Unaccountably, he found himself thinking about religion, although he had no religious convictions whatever. He was particularly haunted by the chapter in the Gospel of St. Matthew which relates the birth of Jesus and the visit of the Wise Men. Who were the Wise Men, he wondered? Where had they come from, and why? He decided to figure

23

out his own conception of the Wise Men from the East.

And so, after much reading and study of the Bible, Wallace wrote an account of the meeting of the Magi in the desert, and their journey to Bethlehem to see the Christchild. When it was finished, he left the manuscript on his desk, undecided what to do with it.

Some time later, on a night in 1876, Wallace was returning home after an evening with friends. He had been listening to a discussion of religion—of God, Jesus, heaven, and eternal life. Wallace had taken little or no part in the argument, for the very good reason that he knew nothing at all about the subject under discussion. Did he believe in God? He did not know. Was Jesus Christ divine? He did not know. Religion had had no place in his active life, and he was totally ignorant about theology.

As he walked home alone in the darkness that evening, Lew Wallace began to regret that ignorance. For the first time in his life he began to feel that religion might be a very important matter. He should believe *something*. But what? How did one find out what to believe? Read sermons? Read theology, on which no two men agreed? No, he would never come to any decision that way. The only thing to do was to read the Bible. As the Bible was the basis for all Christian theology, he would make it the basis for his own religious convictions.

But Wallace knew from experience that he would have to have some definite purpose in studying the Bible—something to keep him interested. He was not a man to study just for the sake of studying. The search for religious convictions alone would not be enough. He needed something else.

For days Wallace mulled the matter over. Then one day an inspiration came. He went to his wife in great excitement.

"My dear, I'm going to write a book."

(to be continued)

The Book That Converted Its Author

Elizabeth Rider Montgomery

Part 2

Note these words:
- substantiate: *to prove true*
- factions: *groups, cliques*
- conquistador (kŏn·kwĭs′tə·dôr′): *Spanish word for "conqueror." Spanish conquistadors had originally explored and claimed what was to become New Mexico.*

Mr. Lew Wallace's ignorance of the Scriptures has brought about his decision to write a book that will cause him to study the Bible.

"That is splendid," his wife replied. "I'm glad you are going to start another book. You enjoyed so much your work on *The Fair God*. What will it be this time?"

"A tale of the Christ," Wallace answered. "I shall use what I wrote about the Wise Men as the beginning of the book, and I shall end with the crucifixion. In between—"

"Yes," prompted his wife. "In between—?"

"Well, I hardly know yet. It will be a story which will show the religious and political condition of the world at the time of Christ."

"But will you have Jesus himself in your story?" asked his wife, troubled. "Won't that be dangerous? I'm afraid you will offend many readers who have their own conception of Christ and will not like to see him pictured differently."

Lew Wallace frowned. "That is one of the greatest obstacles I shall have to hurdle," he agreed. "The only solution I can see at present, is to have a human hero, who is the central figure in the story. The figure of Christ must be in the background, yet He must dominate the book. Well, I shan't worry too much about that just yet. I shall be working on this project a long time, no doubt, and many of my difficulties may smooth themselves out before I come to them."

Wallace was right: he worked on his book a long time. More than seven years. Most of the time was taken up with research, rather than writing. He took infinite

25

pains to verify every fact, to substantiate every statement.

And of course, to make his progress even slower, he had to make a living. Writing was merely spare-time work for him. He was in those years, to begin with, a lawyer, busy enough to suit any man. And then, in 1878, with his book far from finished, he was made governor of the territory of New Mexico. Then, indeed, Wallace knew what it was to be busy. Trying simultaneously to manage a legislature of jealous factions, to take care of an Indian war, and to sell some mines which had been located by the Spanish conquistadors, he found it increasingly difficult to finish his book. Sometimes he could not even start to write before midnight. To cap the climax, in the last months of his work on *Ben-Hur,* he knew that his life was in constant danger. "Billy the Kid" had sworn to kill him.

But Lew Wallace was not a man to let either the pressure

of work of the fear of death keep him from finishing what he had started. Patiently, tirelessly he labored. And at last his book was completed and carefully copied in purple ink. His work was done. Not only that, he had discovered, himself, what he wanted: religious convictions. Lew Wallace, in writing his book of the Christ, had come to believe in Him.

In 1880, *Ben-Hur: A Tale of the Christ* was published by Harper and Brothers. At first it was not popular. Nearly two years passed before its sales started to grow. But at last it began to be appreciated, and before many more years went by it became one of the most popular books of the century.

 565 words

Momentous Decision

Elizabeth Rider Montgomery

 Part 1

Note this word:
mercantile: *having to do with a store and trade*

You may know "The Legend of Sleepy Hollow." Ichabod Crane, Brom Bones, and the Headless Horseman are familiar to many Americans. Not only that, they are known all over the world, for the author was the first American writer to receive recognition abroad. In fact, he was the first American to achieve real success as a writer in our own country. Yet he might never have attained literary fame if he had listened to his devoted family and well-meaning friends.

In 1818, Washington Irving, true American in spirit as well as in name, had been in England for three years. He had come abroad originally because of a halfhearted interest in the family mercantile business, and also because he had been at loose ends in New York and wanted a change of scene.

Of necessity, however, his halfhearted interest in the affairs of P. Irving and Company of Liverpool had immediately become wholehearted, for the business was in bad shape and his brother Peter, manager of the Liverpool office, very ill. For three years Washington Irving had worked hard to save the business, but his efforts were futile. The brothers had been forced into bankruptcy.

Now, in the fall of 1818, with the difficult period of bankruptcy proceeding behind him, Irving took refuge in his sister's home near Birmingham for much-needed rest before facing the future.

One day his sister, Mrs. Van Wart, found him staring out the window with unseeing eyes at the attractive grounds.

"Thinking?" she asked gently.

Irving nodded, turning to smile at this charming youngest sister of their large family.

"Not brooding, I hope," she went on, "over that dreadful bankruptcy business?"

"No," answered Irving. "Not brooding, Sally. That's past and done. We did the best we could, and we failed. No, it isn't the past I'm thinking of; it's the future. I am forced to make a living now, you know. I can no longer depend on the generosity of our brothers."

"The future?" repeated Sally in surprise. "But I thought William was going to find a situation for you?"

Irving smiled slightly. He knew that their brother William was doing everything in his power to obtain the post of Secretary of Legation at the Court of St. James for him. But he also knew he would never accept it.

"Then Ebenezer?" Sally went on anxiously, reading refusal in his face. "He has something in mind for you, hasn't he?"

Irving nodded. At their brother Ebenezer's urging, his old friend Decatur was keeping a place open for him in the Navy Board at home. But that, too, he would refuse.

"Sally," he said earnestly, "try to understand. You mustn't think I am ungrateful. Our brothers mean well. They have been more than good to me, the youngest son. But I cannot accept any of the positions they might find for me. I'm not meant for political offices or for business. I know that now. Literature is my calling, and that is what I mean to follow. I've decided—just today."

"Then you're going to edit that magazine," Sally sighed in relief. "The one that Mr. Murray wants you to take."

"No, Sally," answered Irving firmly. "I am not going to edit what other people write. I'm going to make a living by my own writing. My decision is made."

Sally Van Wart studied her handsome brother fondly. Who would have suspected that such a seemingly easy-going man could be so firm and unyielding? Make a living from writing, Indeed! Why, everyone knew that the only people who made any money from writing were the publishers, who printed anything they wanted to, regardless of copyrights. But if Washington wanted to think he could earn a living with his pen, let him think so. He could always have a home with her family. Her husband would agree, she knew.

(to be continued)

STOP 650 words

29

Momentous Decision

Elizabeth Rider Montgomery

Part 2

Note this word:
deplored: *disapproved of*

Washington Irving has decided to try to earn his living by writing. His family has never heard of a full-time writer before, and they would rather that Washington try some other career.

So Washington made his great decision. In spite of his brothers' disappointment, he turned a deaf ear to all proposals of occupations with assured pay and determined to launch himself into the uncertain career of literature.

Having decided that much, the next question was: what to write? But he knew the answer to that question almost as soon as he asked it. Ever since he had written the *Knickerbocker History of New York* he had been amazed to find out how little most Americans knew of the history and legend of the New York region of their own country. He would write about those old American legends. . . . And he would write about England, too, for he believed that the two English-speaking countries should understand and appreciate each other, instead of being jealous and antagonistic.

Yes, he would write a series of sketches and stories. And he would call his work *The Sketch Book*.

It was not long after this that he got one of his best ideas for this *Sketch Book*. His brother-in-law, Hal Van Wart, had been reminiscing about his youth in New York State.

The conversation turned to Tarrytown.

"I remember the place well," said Irving. "How often I visited my friend Paulding at Tarrytown. Quaint little town, Tarrytown. The Paulding family still spoke Dutch, and the minister at the little church preached in Dutch. They told me some wonderful old legends."

"About the Headless Hessian?" asked Van Wart.

"Oh, yes," nodded Irving. "That was one of their favorites. And of course the Hendrik Hudson legends."

30

"Did they tell you about Brom Bones?" queried the other.

"Brom Bones?" repeated Irving doubtfully. "Why, no, I don't seem to recall that name. Who was he?"

"Well," began Van Wart, settling back in his chair with the air of a man who has a good story to tell, "Brom Bones was a wild young blade who boasted that he feared nothing, neither man nor spirit. One time, so they say . . ." And he went on to tell the legend about the intrepid Brom Bones who had met the headless horseman and run a race with him for a bowl of milk punch.

The story caught Irving's fancy. Immediately his imagination took fire. Hurrying to his room at the conclusion of the tale, he wrote down the framework of a story, "The Legend of Sleepy Hollow."

It was more than a year later, however, before he finished the story. During that year the first parts of *The Sketch Book* had been published. "Rip Van Winkle," one of the first sketches to be printed, had been read, reread, and loved all over America, and in England as well. By the time "The Legend of Sleepy Hollow" came out in 1819, Irving had proved that he could make a living out of his writings. His decision, which his family and his friends deplored, to pass up a dependable income and the responsibilities that went with it, for the freedom and uncertainty of literature, made his name immortal. Moreover, that same decision woke the world to the fact that the United States was a nation in its own right—a nation capable of turning out writers of genius.

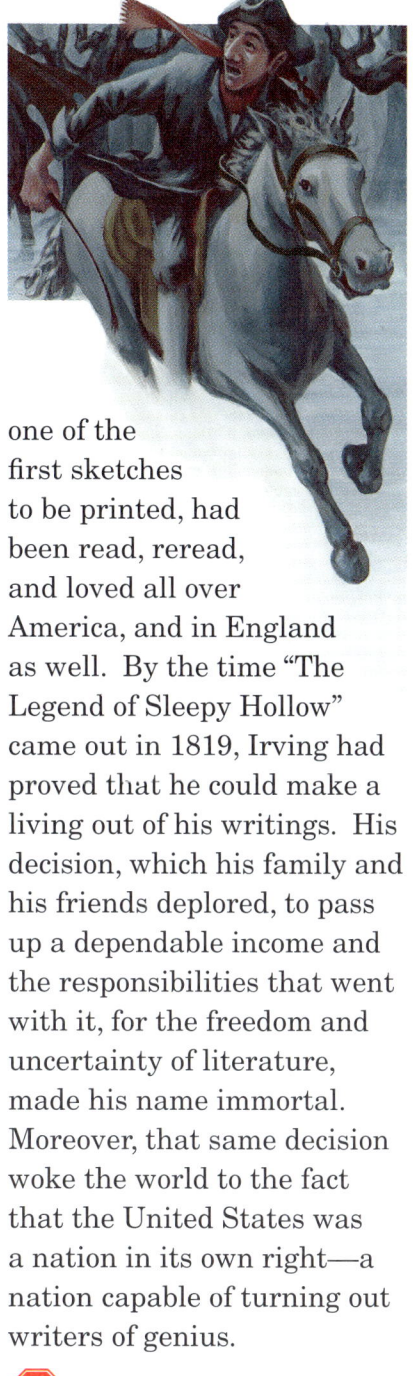

STOP 610 words

He Used His Head

Margaret Applegarth

Part 1

Nobody ever had more exciting things buzzing around in his head than William Carey. On almost any morning the other boys would find him up in his favorite treetop, pretending he was Captain Cook, who in the 1770s was England's most talked about traveler.

"Say, Bill, where's Captain Cook now?" they called, as they scrambled up the branches to reach him. And he would tell them of the latest adventures of the world's greatest explorer, rounding Cape Horn, or landing on cannibal islands, or discovering wild tribes whom nobody in England had ever seen or heard of before. William Carey always lived every adventure as though it were his very own.

"I hear that those natives wear rings in their noses and eat each other up, Bill!" one of his friends would shudder.

"Early Britons, back in Julius Caesar's day, did the same thing. But see how this tribe hollows its boats out of tree trunks. Pretty neat, isn't it? Not one nail in their country. Captain says the bugs over there are as big as his fist...."

"Now Bill's off!" they laughed. For if Captain Cook was Bill Carey's interest, surely bugs, beetles, butterflies, and birds were his love. He would sit for hours watching them as they grew up. He knew what they ate—or turned into. Perhaps you can guess that every cat and dog in town tagged around at William Carey's heels all day.

Another thing, he tried his hand at painting pictures. At first they were simply awful. Boys used to stand around and poke fun at him "What's that, Bill? A house on fire?" But in the end everybody could tell a sunset from a sunflower, and a grasshopper from a steam engine. His friends even began hinting, "I wouldn't mind having that one for keeps, if you don't know what else to do with it."

His friends thought it was hard luck when Bill at fourteen had to begin earning his own living as a shoemaker's apprentice. Cobbling boots, banging nails into tough shoe soles all day, can be a mighty dull job. Over his bench William Carey hung a map of the world, pasted together from old pieces of wrapping paper, and on it he scribbled down the things he had learned about each country from Captain Cook. He began wondering how people talked to each other in other places; and as he sat whacking away he taught himself Latin and Greek and Hebrew. They are really "dead" languages, since nobody speaks them any more. He also learned Dutch and German and French. As you can see, his mind was brimful of ideas. But the liveliest idea of all struck him one day as he looked down at a Bible open beside him on his cobbler's bench. The words that kept blinking up at him were:

"Go ye! Go ye! Go ye! Go ye into all the world!"

Like Captain Cook?

Well, no, not quite! He felt goose pimples all up and down his spine when he began to realize that God by means of that brisk command was telling him that he had no business to stay home in England. The next day he stood up in a big church gathering of Baptists and asked why all the Christians in England had never yet obeyed God's plain command *to go places,* and that as for him, he *wanted* to go.

A man named Deacon Kendrik called to him crossly. "Sit down, young man! If God wants to convert the heathen, He will do it without your help or mine!"

(to be continued)

STOP 590 words

33

He Used His Head

Margaret Applegarth

Part 2

William Carey wanted to be a missionary, but a man in his church told him, "Sit down, young man! If God wants to convert the heathen, He will do it without your help or mine!"

But *sitting down* was the one thing William Carey simply could not do. His mind again began buzzing. How could he stir up people who did not want to be stirred up? How could he get people to take Jesus Christ seriously? Perhaps newspapers would help. He began writing disturbing letters to the various editors, telling them this or that about the various countries of the world, until the readers began to get properly aroused. Then when William Carey stood up again, in another meeting, and asked if somebody in England should not be sent, they voted to send young Carey, himself. They could give him only sixty-eight dollars, and he had miles and miles of sea to cross between England and India, but he felt it was always safe to start on God's errands quickly. The words he said somehow match everything we know about him, even from those early days:

"Expect great things of God, attempt great things for God."

He began to attempt and he began to expect as soon as he arrived in India. But first, there was the stubborn fact that he had no money at all.

He took a job in an indigo factory to earn some. Except what he spent for food, all of the money went for his work.

He did not know a word of Bengali, the language of seventy million Hindus. All right then, follow them around, listen hard, write down words, fill the mind with them, dream about them, use them. So he went all over Calcutta, touching a table, writing down the words people said; pointing to a baby, writing that down; pointing to a snake, writing that down; pointing to an idol, writing that down. Pointing, writing. Pointing, writing. It was endless. Day after day, year after year, he filled his mind with thousands of delightful new words until finally he knew enough to write a fat dictionary.

He did all this just to get ready to start translating the Bible into Bengali.

But there was no paper to print it on. Very well, why not learn to make paper cheaply by boiling up old rags, mashing them, spreading out this messy stuff to dry in the sun? What's a mind for, except to get busy on something nobody else has thought through before?

India was heaping full of such things waiting for somebody to think through. William Carey and his mind tackled them. There were hundreds of other languages spoken all around him, which nobody had ever written down. Very well, he would write them down! He would learn them by heart. He would translate the Bible for these people. Wasn't that why he had come to India?

So William learned to speak 32 different tongues. Ask yourself how one mind could cope with all those new words and have room for anything else. But William had time to notice many forlorn little orphans and homeless children wandering around the streets of Calcutta with nobody to take care of them. Again, he had no money. He started earning it, however, and built an orphanage and a school for these miserable children he had been falling in love with.

At every turn in every street, he saw far too many lepers with far too many sores. And nobody seemed to care. So William Carey cared. For surely if Jesus Christ had gone through Galilee loving lepers and healing them, this was a huge hint that the same thing could be done in India. So William Carey collected some money, and built his lepers their first hospital. It was a cool, clean, decent place. How different and how comfortable for the lepers not to be kicked at by every passer-by.

(to be continued)

STOP 660 words

35

He Used His Head

Margaret Applegarth

Part 3

William Carey had come to India to "attempt great things for God."

Then there was that matter of beauty: Why should streets in India be so ugly? William Carey wasted no time but wrote to England: "Send me a pinch of seeds." What could be better than English daisies and primroses and violets growing in Calcutta?

From every corner of India, Carey collected flowers. Now when he translated out of the New Testament the words, "Consider the lilies, how they grow," people could come to his garden and know how gorgeous they were. So Carey's Botanical Garden became the most famous in the entire Orient, and "Carey's Walk" became a long avenue of rare shade trees—mahogany, deodar, teak and tamarand—for which he had ransacked the world.

It bothered Carey that there were no schools for boys. And the only answer he could find was, "Start them, William, start them!" Why shouldn't boys in India love bugs and learn about them as he had done in England? He began teaching about his beloved bugs and bushes. It seemed sensible also to write special textbooks for his boys about insects, birds, fishes, flowers, animals. Don't ask me how he ever found the time to do it. His lively mind was always taking in somebody's needs and coping quickly with their problems.

For instance, no matter where he looked, people were dreadfully sick, and had no doctor. Very well, why not treat them himself? He learned certain simple remedies, and certain common-sense rules of health, and became a popular doctor.

Then he noticed that half the trouble among India's millions was due to poor food. He wrote to England asking for scythes and sickles and plows and spades, and he began to teach the people of India how to farm.

All this time nobody had become a Christian. William Carey searched his mind to recall what it was that made Jesus Christ so attractive to people. He tried to be just as gentle, just as loving. It was seven long years before a man named Krishna Pal became his first convert. It was really only when Krishna broke his arm that the miracle started. For he was a carpenter by trade, and needed the use of his arm, so he came to William Carey to have the bone set. For six weeks while the broken bone knitted, William Carey talked with Krishna Pal about Jesus Christ. Then came that wonderful day when down at the foot of the Carey garden Krishna Pal was baptized in the River Hoogli. The banks were lined with astonished Hindus, their own minds crammed with a hundred curious questions. Had Krishna lost his mind?

No, God had *found* it, was the answer.

From that moment on, Krishna Pal's mind joined William Carey's in attempting great things for God. The time came when his family and his neighbors and their neighbors discovered for themselves what the Bible means when it says:

"Let this mind be in you which was also in Christ Jesus our Lord."

STOP 515 words

Parable of Patriotism: The Man without a Country

Elizabeth Rider Montgomery

Part 1

Note these words:
- renown: *fame*
- incensed: *furious*
- poetic justice: *an outcome where the bad is punished and the good is rewarded*
- martial law: *the law administered by military forces in a time of emergency (In this story the emergency was war.)*

For fifty years he had not seen his country nor heard her name. He knew nothing that had happened in his homeland during that half century, though he had been constantly surrounded by fellow countrymen. There were thirty-four stars in the flag now, but he knew the names of only half the states they represented. He knew nothing that was going on at home—nothing. For the subject he wanted most to talk about was the one that must never be mentioned in his hearing.

Can you imagine what it would be like to be homeless—forever a wanderer? Do you realize how much your home and your country mean to you? Read "The Man without a Country." Even if you already know the story, read it again. Like our patriotic songs, this story reawakens our love of America, which too often is sleeping.

It is not strange that "The Man without a Country" kindles in the reader a feeling of patriotism; it was intended to do just that. The strange thing about the story is that it brought literary fame to its author, who wanted an entirely different kind of renown.

Edward Everett Hale was first and foremost a minister of the gospel. His life work was preaching about Christ and the kingdom of heaven. But he was deeply interested, too, in the world of here and now. He could never pass up an opportunity to do something to better his earthly world and his fellow men.

When he returned to Boston after a trip to Europe in 1859, Hale was determined to concentrate on his church work to the exclusion of everything else. He would allow no other activities to take his time and energy. In little more than a year, however, the country was plunged into Civil War, and Hale found himself impelled to give a great deal of his time and strength to national affairs.

By birth, training, and inclination, Hale was a Northerner, a Unionist, an antislavery man. He felt that he had to help the Union cause and support the government of Abraham Lincoln, the President, in every way he could. He worked in the Sanitary Commission of the army, helped with the Refugee's Aid, Freedman's Aid, and Emigrant Aid. These activities took a great deal of time and thought away from his church work.

In addition, Hale helped the Union cause by writing. He had a standing agreement with Fields, editor of the *Atlantic Monthly,* that he would write articles to help keep up people's courage during those difficult days. Since the North was apparently losing in the early years of the war, Unionists were very disheartened. Thus these morale-building articles were important to keep people working and fighting.

One day in 1863 something happened which convinced Hale that a powerful article on patriotism was absolutely essential. An Ohio

39

politician, by the name of Vallandigham, asserted publicly that he did not want to belong to a country that did things Lincoln and the government were doing.

How incensed Hale was when he heard that!

"Does not want to belong to our country, indeed!" he cried. "Merely because he disagrees with what the President has said, or disapproves of what he had done! For *that,* Vallandigham is ready to give up his country. I wonder if he realizes what his life would be if he had no country to love and work for?"

If one man could feel as Vallandigham did, there might be others who felt the same way. In that case, the fire of patriotism must be merely dying embers and should be fanned into flame. He would write something that would do it.

While he was still mulling over this idea, Vallandigham received his punishment, which seemed like poetic justice to Hale: General Burnside, who was in command in Ohio (since the state was under martial law), arrested Vallandigham and sent him into the Confederate lines. He said the North did not want such people; perhaps the South did.

And then Hale knew what his article to arouse patriotism would be: it would be the story of a man such as Vallandigham—a man who wanted nothing further to do with his country.

(to be continued)

705 words

Parable of Patriotism: The Man without a Country

Elizabeth Rider Montgomery

Part 2

Note these words:
- acquitted: *freed of the charge*
- aspire: *desire and work toward*
- impetuous: *headstrong and impulsive*
- ironical: *having a different result than what was expected*

Hoping to arouse patriotism during the Civil War, Edward Everett Hale has decided to write a story about what happened to a man who said he wanted nothing more to do with his country.

So Edward Everett Hale, the Boston minister, set to work getting material for his story. He read all he could find about every traitor and every suspected traitor the United States had fathered, especially Aaron Burr. He became particularly interested in the account of Burr's dealings with General Wilkinson who, during the 1790s and early 1800s, was secretly in the pay of the King of Spain while commanding the army of the United States in the Mississippi Valley. Aaron Burr was acquitted of the charges of treason brought against him in the famous treason trial at Richmond; Wilkinson was merely suspected of treason during his lifetime and was never formally charged with it, but after his death he was proved to have been a traitor.

None of the traitors or potential traitors of history satisfied Hale, however, as a central figure for his story. Eventually he created his own traitor, a young lieutenant in the United States Army who declared he wished never to hear of the United States again. In casting about for a name for his imaginary character, Hale remembered the Captain Nolan who had been a friend of the traitor Wilkinson. So he called his man without a country Philip Nolan.

After Hale had planned his story, but before he had written it, the exiled politician, Vallandigham, was nominated for governor of Ohio. To Hale that was unthinkable.

That a man who had publicly announced his scorn of the United States should aspire to be governor of one of those states! He must not be elected.

At once Hale went to his friend Fields, the editor of the *Atlantic Monthly*.

"Vallandigham must not win that election," he told him determinedly. "He is not fit for a public office."

"Without a doubt you are right," agreed Fields. "But he will probably lose the election."

"We must see to it that he *does* lose it," insisted Hale.

"But how?" asked the editor. "What can we do? The *Atlantic* is not a newspaper, to campaign against a candidate."

"Sometimes stories are more powerful than editorials," observed Hale. "I have a story in mind that might have some influence. It is about a man who has said he wants nothing more to do with his country. This would be a good time for it."

"Yes, it would," agreed the editor. "How soon could you have it ready?"

"In time for the September issue."

"That would do," nodded Fields. "Then it would be out in time for the October election. We shall hope it will influence public opinion as we wish."

So Hale wrote "The Man without a Country." And it was immediately set up in type. But unforeseen circumstances prevented Fields from using it when he had planned. Hale's story had no chance to prove that it could influence public opinion against Vallandigham, who was hopelessly defeated without its aid.

But the story was printed at last in the December issue, 1863. And it did much to strengthen the Union cause. The story of an impetuous young man who plotted against his country, denounced her, and spent the rest of his life repenting it roused all who read it to a new appreciation of the United States.

In later years Edward Everett Hale often regretted the fact that he was remembered and pointed out as the author of a short story, when most of his life had been spent preaching the gospel. Perhaps it is ironical that his fame should rest on a product of his patriotism rather than on his truly great sermons. But like other famous parables, Hale's "Man without a Country," a parable of patriotism, did more good than many a sermon in his country's hour of need.

STOP 655 words

Inseparable Brothers
Elizabeth Rider Montgomery

Part 1

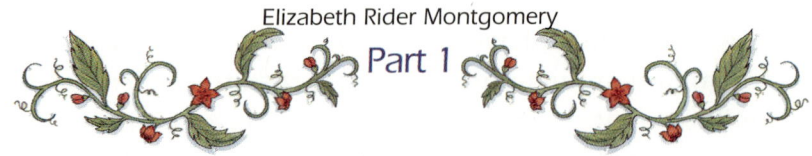

Note these words:
> stupendous: *marvelous*
> unprepossessing: *not creating a great impression*

The name "Grimm" means fairy tales to the world. Everyone knows *Grimms' Fairy Tales*. Everyone remembers "Snow White," "Hansel and Gretel," "The Town Musicians of Bremen," and all the other stories that we associate with the name of Grimm.

Grimms' fairy tales are stories that were told and retold for generations in Germany. But they might have been forgotten and lost forever (for the art of storytelling seemed to be dying out) if two brothers had not taken it upon themselves to gather these tales and preserve them for the people of their native land, and—although they did not know it—for the children of the world.

In the early 1800s Jakob and Wilhelm Grimm were librarians at their home town of Kassel, Germany. Sometimes people smiled to see the two young men always together. The Grimm brothers roomed together; they worked together; they spent their leisure hours together.

But the brothers did not mind the smiles of their townspeople. Several years before, as boys studying in Paris, they had resolved never to separate. And they meant to keep that vow. So they went their quiet, cheerful way without explanation or apology.

While people may have found amusing the fact that the two were inseparable, they had nothing but respect for the young men themselves. For everyone knew that the Grimm brothers were the most learned scholars the town had produced. Their knowledge of languages, grammar, the history of words, and the history of literature was stupendous for men in their early twenties.

It was not long, however, before the brothers were doing something that their neighbors thought even stranger than always being together: they, the scholarly, the educated, were frequently seen talking with the ignorant, the uneducated people of the district—peasants, servants, shepherds. However, this queer behavior, too, was the result of a resolution. At the same time they vowed never to separate, the Grimm brothers had decided that the aim of their lives should be a revival of ancient German literature. A great deal of study had convinced them that most of the old literature of their country had never been written down. It existed only in the minds of living people who had heard it from others now dead, who had heard it from others long since dead. Consequently, they reasoned, the only way to revive the ancient learning was to talk to living persons who might know these old tales. And those people were the illiterates, the ones who could not read for themselves and hence must get stories by word of mouth.

That was why Jakob and Wilhelm Grimm were so often seen talking to all sorts of poor and lowly people: tramps, wagoners, maids, nurses. For one could never tell, the Grimms had found, who was a natural-born storyteller. The most unprepossessing head might contain a priceless store of old tales.

The brothers were well fitted for this self-appointed task. Wilhelm was a friendly fellow, a good conversationalist, and an excellent storyteller, who could get people to talking. And Jakob's knowledge of languages enabled him to talk to each person in his own dialect. Both were so honest, so simple and unassuming, that rich and poor, educated and illiterate, liked and trusted them at sight.

550 words *(to be continued)*

Inseparable Brothers
Elizabeth Rider Montgomery

Part 2

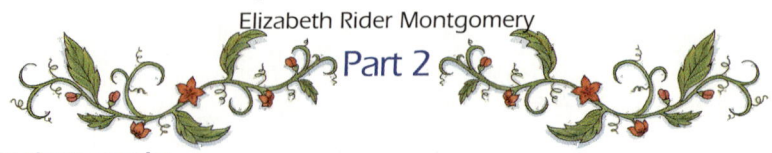

Note these words:
veritable: *real*
Niederzwehrn (nē′der·zvärn′)
ponderous: *very large and heavy*

Jakob and Wilhelm Grimm were determined to write down the old German literature which existed only in the heads of the German folk.

For months the brothers patiently continued to search out possible story sources. Progress was slow. They found a tale here and one there. But many trails led to nothing. They hunted up a shepherd in one district who was supposed to know the old stories, only to find that it had been his father, now dead, who knew them; the son had never bothered to remember his father's stories. They traveled to a small town miles away to talk to a cobbler, but he could tell them only the tales they had already gathered.

But one day they stumbled on a veritable gold mine of stories. In the village of Niederzwehrn, near Kassel, they met a nurse, the wife of a cowherd by the name of Viehmannin—a vigorous, pleasant woman with clear, penetrating eyes.

"I know the old stories," she told them confidently. "I have all of them in my head. It is a gift not granted to many, to know these stories," she added simply.

"Yes," agreed Jakob. "Few have the knack of remembering the old stories just as they were told to them."

"But I do," insisted the peasant. "I tell them always the same—exactly as they were told to me. I am the granddaughter of a granddaughter of the greatest storyteller of Zwehrn."

"Then you are the very person we are looking for," smiled Wilhelm in relief. "Would you tell us some of these old tales?"

"I would be glad to," replied Viehmannin promptly. "I love to tell them."

46

And without more ado she motioned her callers to a rude seat and began the story of "The Fisherman and His Wife."

As she related the tale it was obvious that she had told it many times before. She never hesitated for a word but seemed to know the story by heart, word for word.

When she had finished, the brothers looked at each other. It was not necessary to speak. Each knew what was in the other's mind: Here at last they had found someone who could undoubtedly supply a large amount of the material they were looking for. A born storyteller, a direct descendant of one of those storytellers who had kept alive the ancient literature of Germany.

Wilhelm turned to the woman again. "That was excellent. You told it superbly."

"I told it as it was told to me," repeated Viehmannin. "I always tell it the same way."

47

"Would you mind," asked Wilhelm hesitantly, "would you mind repeating it—a little more slowly—so that I can write it down just the way you tell it?"

"I would be glad to," answered the peasant. And slowly, deliberately, she began again the tale of "The Fisherman and His Wife," while Wilhelm wrote it down as fast as he could.

Day after day, as often as Viehmannin could spare the time, the Grimm brothers returned to listen to her stories. Story after story Wilhelm wrote down exactly as she told it. And by the time she had exhausted the stock she carried in her head, they had quite a pile of manuscript and felt they were well launched on their project.

By this time, too, the news of the Grimm brothers' undertaking had gone around. People in all walks of life had become interested in it and sent them stories, or directed them to others who could supply them. Their collection grew and grew. In 1812 they had the first book of stories published, under the title of *Kinder-und-Hausmarchen*, or *Tales for Children and Household*.

For years they worked on their collection. They tracked down folk tales as hunters stalk game. They gathered two hundred fairy tales. Although collected for adults, the stories were eagerly read by children all over Germany. Soon the tales were translated into other languages. Eventually they were read all over the world.

Though both Jakob and Wilhelm lived to be old men and wrote many scholarly books such as a German dictionary, a ponderous grammar, and so on, to the world their names will forever mean fairy tales. Thus today, as during their lives, the brothers Grimm are inseparable.

STOP 715 words

Johnny-Jump-Up

Margaret Applegarth

Part 1

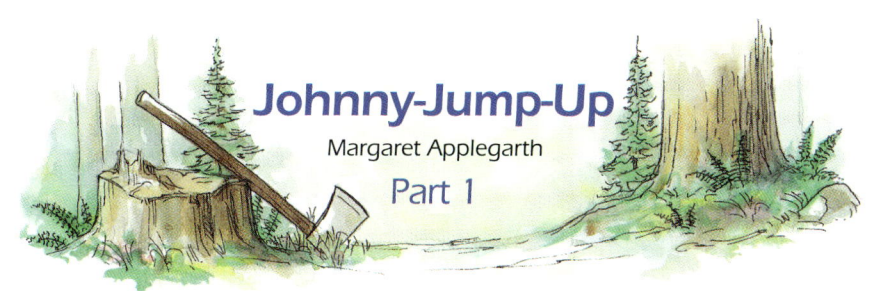

Note this word:
primeval: *ancient*

Unless you have been brought up by a gang of lumberjacks, you have no idea how tiresome it is to be nicknamed "Johnny-Jump-Up" and hear nothing else all day but "Johnny, jump up and fetch me this," "Johnny, jump up and fetch me that."

So the real Johnny was on the jump all day. Johnny tramped through that forest primeval, from the tall trees where the men were working back to their camp, fetching great canteens of coffee; fetching another axe; another coat; more rope; more chains. There was always something needed and Johnny was on the jump all day to fetch it.

Hurrying back and forth through the lonely woods was not an easy walk. He was the only human being among all those giant trees. Ten thousand branches overhead stretched downward as if ready to catch him. Not one branch creaked, not one twig trembled, not one leaf moved. The silence was overwhelming. When the mighty forest did not scare him with its terrible bigness and loneliness, it bored him. Johnny had ideas buzzing in his head, but nobody in that entire lumber camp had time to listen.

Since no one else would listen, Johnny talked to Ah Wing, the Chinese cook. This wasn't much good either. For Ah Wing went round and round stirring his big kettles, standing on tiptoe to look anxiously into each pot. After Johnny had talked and talked, Ah Wing would grunt, "Unk-unk!" It never made much sense to Johnny (although your Chinese may be better).

"Some day," Johnny used to vow to himself, "I'll say something to make those fellows sit up and take notice." But how could anything out in this forgotten neck of the woods be exciting enough to budge them one inch? Then as he was

49

staggering toward the forest with Ah Wing's big coffee canteen for the men's lunch, a wild idea popped into his head. How would it be to dash up and yell "Fire"? Then see what happens.

He left the canteen behind and started running pell-mell toward the sound of axes and the crash of falling timber. He dashed up and yelled loudly, *"Fire! Fire!* Down by the Hollow Rock cabins!"

It worked like a charm.

Tuxedo Tex dropped his axe. Slippy Sam ran toward him. Everybody began sliding down tree trunks and hurrying over: Where? Where was the fire?

Johnny panted out an enormous tale, and almost believed it himself so thrilled was he to see them tear madly off toward Hollow Rock. The woods were dry as tinder, due to lack of rain. So they feared the worst. Johnny stayed behind and had a good laugh. It was funny to see axes left midway through a tree trunk, and lunch pails left open for the ants, and plaid coats left behind on the underbrush.

Then he remembered that he too had left something midway, and he started back for the canteen and Ah Wing. But somehow as he staggered along, bent over by his burden, his marvelous plan began to dwindle and dwindle until he felt like a dwarf. "Sort of dumb, really, if you ask me!" he admitted to himself, and felt crestfallen to think he hadn't thought up something steeper. This one would be over in a minute.

Ah Wing took the big tin with surprise at finding it still full. "Didn't they like the coffee?" he asked.

Johnny told him the joke. Ah Wing shook his head sadly. "Johnny, you'll get a good licking out of all this!" And instantly Johnny realized how true his words were.

Johnny was confined to his room for several days after the men returned. The wind in the treetops was all he heard by day, or squirrels scampering on the roof. Then things grew normal again. He himself grew wonderfully proper and polite.

Meanwhile there was no rain. The weather grew drier and drier. It was a month later. Off in the distant woods, chopping and sawing as usual, the men suddenly saw Johnny come lapping toward them yelling, *"Fire! Fire!* Licking up the timber piles down by the sawmill!"

The lumberjacks guffawed, "At it again, sonny? Yell louder!"

"Think you're going to catch us twice with the same old yarn, do you? Think up a new one."

Johnny waved his arms like a windmill. "But this time, it's true, I tell you—down by the sawmill! It's horrible—all that timber! Hurry——*hurry!*"

But nobody budged.

"Holler like you really meant it, kid," drawled Hesitation Harry in his lazy voice.

So Johnny really hollered, and yanked elbows, and pummeled chests. "It's crackling and hissing down there!" he cried. "It's red hot and roaring and sizzling! The smoke blinded me! I ran all the way! Hurry!"

But nobody budged.

"Keep it up, Johnny! Tell us again! A little louder, boy, you sound sorta weak."

Suddenly, he was altogether weak, tumbling into a pale little heap as a strange blackness came over his eyes. The men looked at him, puzzled. Was this all play-acting, too? But Slippy Sam leaned over and said, "Fellows, his clothes are full of wood smoke!"

(to be continued)

STOP 865 words

51

Johnny-Jump-Up

Margaret Applegarth

Part 2

Johnny had tricked the lumberjacks once; so they didn't believe him when he yelled "Fire!" in earnest.

Everybody tore off to the fire, but it was too late. Already the timber was one mass of flames—rolling, creeping, sucking, crackling, roaring. The red tongues leaped hungrily from pile to pile, hissing, exploding into more flames.

Ten hours later the men tramped back to camp, drank Ah Wing's coffee, then dropped exhausted into their bunks. Poor Johnny crept around on tiptoe, rehearsing all the excuses he could think up, such as, "It probably didn't waste much more than ten minutes—your not believing me, at first."

But no, that was tame stuff. Be gruff. Bluster around. Say, "Now my good men, kindly remember...."

Nonsense! Nobody could talk that way to such tough guys. They would probably punish him again.

To his surprise nobody mentioned the incident again. Instead, Tuxedo Tex merely hauled out his funny little old trunk and began unpacking it.

"Boys," said Tuxedo Tex, "ain't it a fact that this here kid is motherless, fatherless, brotherless, sisterless? Ain't it a fact that since his mammy died while cooking for this here camp nobody ain't ever brought the poor lad up, proper? How about us learning him a little gospel truth from this here Good Book which my Aunt Amelia willed me instead of her money? For now you and me had really ought to be parents to this here lad, if it ain't too late!"

"Never too late to mend, I always says," Slippy Sam nodded.

Old Man Jones sighed, "Back East, a feller Johnny's age goes to Sunday school, regular."

Tuxedo Tex was not through. "Let's me and you aim to turn Johnny-Jump-Up into the truthfulest kid west of the Rockies. Half for our own sakes—so me and you will know whether it's safe to believe him; and half for his ma's sake. She was a mighty good sort. Remember how she always wore a clean white apron, come Sundays? And how she hummed hymns while she cooked? Reckon she'd be scandalized over me letting her son be a heathen."

"Hear! Hear!"

"Count on me!"

"Same here!"

"We'll fetch him up good and proper."

"I don't want to be fetched up good and proper," Johnny cried.

"Oh, yes you do, Johnny! You'll like reading in this here Bible. It's a mighty fine Book, and my Aunt Amelia knew it by heart."

"I don't want to be no Aunt Amelia!" growled poor Johnny, horrified at what the Book might do to him.

But he had to take it; and while sixty eyes were on him, he had to sit and turn the pages.

"Start toward the rear," Tuxedo Tex ordered. "It's easier going, back there."

So Johnny opened there, and then jumped up of his own accord. *"Look!"* he shouted. "Here's something by someone named *John*—did you know that a fellow with my name wrote part of the Bible?"

The men were as surprised as he was. "Really?" they asked.

"Yes, and he is writing about still another John. Listen." Johnny read slowly, "There was a man sent from God whose name was John."

53

"There you are!" cried Tuxedo Tex. "Just you keep your eye glued on him."

* * *

So Johnny kept his eye on John the Baptist. As you know, it is quite a story. But a king finally had him beheaded because he kept telling brave things which really had to be told. After he was gone everybody said, "John did no miracle, but all things that he said of this Man are true."

"Get that, Johnny? Everything John said was—*true!* You better take him for your model."

"But he lost his head, Tex! That's awful risky. Now there's someone else here in John's book whose name is Jesus—there's a lot about Him. Is He the one you fellows are always talking about?"

A guilty look flashed over thirty red faces. Johnny was surprised. "What's got into everybody? You look embarrassed. Did I say something wrong?"

Tuxedo Tex cleared his throat. "Johnny, forget it. We're a lot of bums, us guys are. We're odds and ends of men, too far from home. We ain't got proper talk for a kid to hear. We should never have used the name of Jesus like we did. *He's God, really.* He's the Savior of the world. And from now on any fellow in this camp who ever swears again is going to get in Dutch with me. Is that fair and square?"

Everybody nodded.

Johnny thought, "Only last month I wanted somebody to talk to me. And now they all talk to me, like I mattered. This Book sorta did it!"

Johnny jumped up. "And I'm the kid who wanted something special to happen. Why, here it is! Our men are cleaning up their talk for my sake, so I can turn out to be a credit to my mother and so I won't tell lies."

He began wondering. Were they all writing some new gospel of John, maybe? In a lumber camp? After all, it was a wilderness, wasn't it? And maybe he was a voice crying in that wilderness: "Make straight the way of the Lord. . . . John did no miracle; but all things that John spake of this Man were true. And many believed on Him there."

Even in a lumber camp.

STOP 905 words

The Games Begin!

Rosemary K. Updyke

Note these words:
>contingent: *representative*
>imperceptibly: *slightly, so as not to be noticed*
>studiously: *diligently and deliberately*
>chalice: *a large, decorative cup; a goblet*

On July 6, the long-anticipated 1912 Olympic Games in Sweden were opened by King Gustav V, whose country was hosting this fifth modern Olympiad.

It was a jubilant occasion as teams from twenty-eight nations marched through the main gateway of the city's beautiful new stadium. The stirring strains of "A Mighty Fortress Is Our God" wafted over audience and contestants as the competing athletes strode in along the cinder path. Among America's Olympic hopefuls marched Jim Thorpe and Louis Tewanima, the two young competitors from the Carlisle Indian School. Each contingent marched smartly behind the flowing flag of their country. As they passed the royal enclosure, they paid their respects to King Gustav, Prince Gustav Adolph, and Grand Duke Dimitri of Russia.

The hosts gave welcoming speeches. And then, the Games were declared open!

The following day, more than twenty thousand sports enthusiasts filled the newly created double-decker Olympic Stadium. Europeans in the audience had arrived at the Olympics feeling certain that their Scandinavian sprint stars would easily capture the track titles.

Instead, they watched in awe as American athlete Jim Thorpe dominated the games after diving enthusiastically into the grueling five-event pentathlon. He won the broad jump and the 200-meter dash, as well as the discus throw. He lost only one match, to Sweden's Hugo Weislander in the throw of the javelin.

For the fifth event, Jim had drawn an unfortunate starting slot, positioning him in the next-to-outside lane. As a result, Ferdinand Bie of Norway and Avery Brundage of the United States became the favored contenders.

Jim, dressed in his track uniform of white shorts with a shield-emblazoned white top, took his place at the starting line. Planting the toe of his left shoe firmly on his mark, his right foot spaced back for the push-off, he waited. Outwardly calm, he peered along the imposing stretch of track that lay before him.

In his mind's eye he could clearly see his father's face; he could just as easily hear Hiram's voice. Whether it concerned Jim's school grades, or games with friends— whatever Jim attempted—his father had always urged him to do his best. "Always remember," he would say, impressing Jim with pride in his heritage, "you are an Indian. Show them what an Indian can do!" Recalling the words, Jim imperceptibly nodded agreement as he stood ready for the race.

Anticipation heightened in the stands as fans watched the contenders take their places at the starting line, poised and ready. For each of the seven, it was an awesome moment.

Then the starting shot rang out.

Unlike Thorpe, who cantered off from an unexpectedly slow start, his teammate Brundage and Norway's Bie burst forth in the predicted struggle for the lead. Elbows close to their sides, the two churned off to a fast pace, rounding the track in the first lap.

Thorpe, meanwhile, continued to run farther back in the pack than expected. Keenly aware of his position, he studiously paced himself, all the while assessing his competitors. The seven were well into the second lap when Brundage began slowing noticeably. The Norwegian, Bie, immediately seized the lead.

Thorpe realized that that was the moment he must make his move. Accelerating his pace, he began to move steadily past one contender after another. Sports fans in the stadium were on their feet, breaths held in anticipation as they watched Thorpe, in the third lap, continue that burst of speed and close the gap. Then he breezed past Bie, flinging himself across the finish line several yards ahead of the nearest runner.

Deafening cheers from the crowd poured forth for the American who had proved himself a winner that day with his feats of unequaled speed, endurance, and ability.

While Thorpe was capturing records in his events, his Carlisle teammate, Louis Tewanima, was also making a name for himself. With Jim lustily cheering him on from the sidelines, Tewanima took second place in the strenuous 10,000-meter race. This earned him an Olympic silver medal.

Because of so many other events on the day's schedule, the Games had to be extended one more day, during which Jim placed second in the discus throw, third in the pole vault, and third with the javelin.

Thorpe, who always strove to win at anything he attempted, was dissatisfied with his showing that day. But when the judges huddled to total the scores, American Jim Thorpe was found to have captured an incredible 8,412.96 points out of a possible 10,000! Scoring nearest to Thorpe's total was Sweden's Hugo Wieslander with 7,724 points.

In the afternoon, before the stadium filled with cheering fans, Thorpe was called to the carpeted victory podium. King Gustav placed a laurel wreath upon Jim's head and presented him with a gold medal for his pentathlon win. In addition, the king presented a life-size bust of himself, measuring four feet by twenty-two inches, to the surprised young athlete.

Later, Thorpe was called to the podium to receive his second gold medal and laurel wreath. This time the king also presented him with a gift from the czar of Russia, a spectacular two-foot-long, eighteen-inch-high chalice weighing thirty pounds, lined with gold and embedded with precious jewels and formed in the shape of a Viking ship.

As the king enthusiastically shook Thorpe's hand that second time, he made an emotional declaration with words that would forever after be connected with Jim Thorpe. "Sir," he said, "you are the greatest athlete in the world!"

STOP   920 words

Can Do. Will Do. Did!

Margaret Applegarth

Part 1

Note these words:
din: *give by repetition*
placard: *a poster*
sampan: *a small boat used in the Orient*

Long before the Navy Seabees dreamed up their slogan, "Can do," Jonathan Goble dared to try all sorts of impossible things. It all began one dark night when Jonathan waved his hand to the other sailors on board his ship, grinned, and jumped overboard.

"What does Jonathan think he's made of, to risk such a dangerous way of getting into Japan?" one of the sailors asked, as they heard the splash below, and dimly saw a white figure swimming toward the distant shore.

Nobody had the answer to that question, so another sailor exploded, "Tell me why on earth he wants to go? It's beyond common sense for a man to risk his neck this way, when even the signposts along the shore all carry the same grim warning against coming into Japan!"

"Well, Goble can't say we didn't din it into his head all afternoon. I should think he must know those placards by heart:

> So long as the sun shall warm the earth, let no Christian be so bold as to come to Japan; and let all know that the King of Spain himself, or the Christian's God, or the great God of All, if he violate this command shall pay for it with his head.

Plain enough talk, if you ask me!"

"And Jonathan thinks he can get away with it! But you can't ignore a notice like that!"

So, blue as the Japanese bay in which they were anchored, they all went down to their bunks. But in the morning there on deck, dripping wet but as good as new, was Jonathan Goble.

"Jonny!" they shouted. "So you changed your mind like a sensible fellow?"

"No! I got ashore all right. The only trouble was that the night was so still that the guard heard me swimming. He was standing on the sand with a lantern to meet me when I hit the beach. Although we couldn't understand each other's language, he must have figured that I had fallen overboard by mistake; so he got an old sampan and poled me back here as soon as it was light enough to spot our ship. Mighty decent fellow really!"

"Well, you got off easy, my boy—to come back here with your head still screwed on. So I guess you've learned your lesson all right, and you'll leave Japan alone."

But Jonathan Goble had not learned it, yet. He went on swabbing decks and climbing the rigging. But underneath his cap he was busy every minute wondering if tonight was not the best time to try it again. A moonless night, and the tide would be going his way. The crew were thunderstruck.

"But see here, Jonny, only cats have nine lives. Why risk your one and only body in such a bad business. Remember those signboards!"

"What I remember is how good that Japanese guard was to me! You know how it is, when something tells you 'Go,' why, then, you obey orders; and I've got my orders; so I'll be dropping overboard as soon as it gets dark enough."

Nobody could do a thing to stop him. "At least, don't look so happy!" they said, crossly.

He seemed surprised. "Look here, this isn't exactly happiness, fellows! It's just every bone and nerve and muscle ready to go. Like running a race, maybe."

"But you *can't* win this race, Jonny!"

"Who says I can't?"

"Those Japanese signboards!"

Jonathan Goble grinned at them. "You're a bunch of sweet little old ladies, trying to scare me stiff. Don't you see it's my duty to go?"

But nobody saw. And when he dropped overboard this second time, they tiptoed down to their bunks very quietly, each sailor thinking: If I'm a sweet little old lady, then he's a rash young kid. Nobody could bear to think of Jonny losing his head . . . And for what, please tell us that, *for what?*

Therefore, in the morning it was suprising enough to have their headless sailor back on deck, head and all, dripping wet as before, and with practically the same story. The shores seemed lined with eagle-eyed sentries. This second one—a hundred miles from the first—hardly knew what to do with one lonely young sailor, who seemed to have come for no bad purpose. But he too returned Jonathan Goble politely to the ship out on the horizon.

"So here I am," he announced.

"And here you'd better stay!" they shouted.

"Take the hint, Goble, and play safe from now on."

But that was just what Jonathan Goble could not do. There must be some more foolproof plan for landing in Japan without being noticed. And he must find it!

(to be continued)

STOP 780 words

Can Do. Will Do. Did!
Margaret Applegarth
Part 2

Note these words:
- **hardtack:** *a type of hard bread*
- **gob:** *slang word for sailor*
- **Yedo Bay:** *Tokyo Bay*

Jonathan Goble is determined to get into Japan even though it may mean his death!

All day Jonathan swabbed decks and polished brass and climbed rigging trying to think up a plan, until finally it came to him. How about being nailed up inside a barrel and dumped overboard? Then the waves would carry the barrel inshore? No one would suspect a barrel, bobbing innocently around. Then, of course, the moment it bumped on the beach he could take his hatchet, split up the slats, climb out, and go about his business. He searched the ship for a suitable barrel, stuffed his pockets with hardtack, grabbed a hatchet, and squeezed himself in.

"Nail it up, carefully, boys!" he ordered.

But nobody budged.

"You're crazy!" they growled.

"It's a long way to shore, what's to keep you from dying from lack of air? They tell me a body can't live four minutes without it!"

"What's to keep me from making a hole in the top of the barrel with my hatchet?"

"Wonderful! Wonderful! And what's to keep the whole Pacific Ocean from coming in on you?"

"I can still swim, can't I?"

They argued back and forth, but finally they nailed him in, and lowered the barrel gently into the sea. It was a very silent crew which stood on deck watching the tide carry the keg on its long journey. Nobody knew quite what he was feeling this time—was it awe? or admiration or pity? For this was such pluck as none of them had seen before on land or sea. And all they really guessed was that something far bigger than himself had made Jonathan Goble forget that he was Jonathan Goble, able-bodied seaman, five-foot-seven-inches tall,

160 pounds, brown hair, blue eyes. There was something plus in all this—to want something as badly as Jonny wanted it. But what? *What was it?* which made a man so reckless, when saving one's own skin was everybody's rule for living?

So they pitied the poor sailor on a night like this, being rolled about, bumped and bruised. Moreover, what was to keep him from landing too dizzy to hack his way out? Or too injured not to be caught and tortured and beheaded? A third escape from the sword was more than anybody could hope for.

Nobody slept.

But it is written in the history books that Jonathan Goble was brought back this third time, also. For again the sentries on shore were shocked to spot a barrel riding the breakers, then tossed on the beach, and to see emerging from it a curious dark blue object.

"She rolled on shore as light as an egg," Jonny explained. "And there was I, breaking through like a newborn chick. The sentries were startled out of their boots to see a sailor hatch out, but they were decent chaps. They decided my cruel shipmates had taken this wicked way of getting rid of me. Their code of honor made them go to the trouble to get the poor stranger back to the ship where he belonged. So here I am!"

Nobody said a word. So Jonathan Goble said it for them.

"Now I can see for myself that God does not like His jobs done in these secret, undercover ways. I must discover a plan for getting into Japan with His complete approval. You will surely be relieved!"

The crew had never felt happier. They went around

63

all day whistling their favorite sea-chanty, "Give us more time to blow the man down!" For if anybody refused to "blow down" easily, it was Jonathan Goble. It was grand to have such a hero on board, but when would he try his next wild stunt? And would it be by land or by sea?

It was by land. There were no barrels nor head-chopping placards, but Jonathan Goble went into action around the state of Massachusetts the moment his ship docked in Boston. For you can imagine his excitement when he heard that the United States Government was planning to send Commodore Perry over to Japan to try to persuade that hermit nation to open its ports for American commerce, even removing its signposts.

Jonathan Goble had every intention of going along. He wore his feet out, visiting senators, congressmen, preachers, teachers, lawyers, to tell them that they must write to the President explaining about one able-bodied seaman the Commodore needed on his flagship. He wore his own hand out writing other letters. He wore his voice out, explaining why he longed to go. The members of his church saw through him at once. "That wonderful young Goble is simply a modern Apostle Paul. You can easily imagine his saying just what Paul said, 'I do not account my life of any value nor as precious to myself, if only I may accomplish my course and the ministry which I received from the Lord Jesus, to testify to the gospel of the grace of God.'"

So everybody really did turn heaven and earth to remind the President of Jonathan. And who was that spotless young gob on deck when Commodore Perry's flagship steamed into Yedo Bay on July 8? Who but the same sailor who had once tried barging into Japan in a barrel. Now, however, guns were booming in greeting; fishing-junks began gathering excitedly. Perry sent word that he would never leave until he could meet the Emperor and hand him the treaty of friendship from the President of the United States.

925 words

(to be continued)

Can Do. Will Do. Did!

Margaret Applegarth

Part 3

Note this word:

pomp: *splendor, magnificence*
jinrikisha (jĭn·rĭk′shô′)

Jonathan Goble finally got to Japan! The United States government had sent Commodore Perry to try to convince Japan to trade with America, and Jonathan had sailed with him.

Jonathan Goble pictured himself walking down a Japanese street any day now. As usual, however, he was much too hasty. Often God does His work more slowly than quick young bodies like. But while he stood waiting on deck, Jonathan was thrilled when Sunday morning came and certain high Japanese officials came to call. The Commodore sent word that Americans never did business on that day, for that was when they worshiped God. A Bible was then laid on the Stars and Stripes; the ship's band played "Old Hundred"; and all the sailors sang at the top of their voices:

Before Jehovah's awful
  throne
Ye nations bow with sacred
  joy;
Know that the Lord is God
  alone;
He can create, and He
  destroy.

"Perfect!" one sailor found himself thinking. "What words could tell it better? But still, how I do want to get on shore and get busy telling this story, myself."

However, it was Commodore Perry who went ashore. You never saw such enormous pomp and ceremony as the day when he went to put our President's letter into the Emperor's hands. Jonathan Goble was in ecstasy. "I'll be there in Japan tomorrow, perhaps," he thought. It was alarming, therefore, to find his ship actually sailing away. Good gracious, why?

It seemed that the Commodore felt that the Emperor ought to have some time to think over the treaty. At the end of that time, he promised to come back.

65

"And so will I!" Jonathan Goble said to himself. But meanwhile he was dreadfully discouraged. "What on earth can a fellow do with so many empty days, and not one thing to do but wait?"

His answer was hiding down below decks. For two days later some sailors found a young Japanese stowaway, so hungry that he had come out for food. Nobody knew what to do with him—except Jonathan Goble. . . .

"Give him to me!" he cried. "If I can't live in Japan, let Japan live with me!"

The Japanese boy taught his language to Jonathan, who then told him about God.

Jonathan began translating the Gospel of Matthew into Japanese, with his new friend helping him with every word. When they came to the twenty-fifth verse of chapter 6, the young man from Japan said, "Why it's about *you!*" for it read: "Therefore I say unto you, Take no thought for your life, what ye shall eat, nor yet for your body, what ye shall put on. Is not the life more than meat, and the body than raiment?"

When they had translated the last two verses of the last chapter, which says: "Go ye therefore, and teach all nations. . . ," the Japanese stowaway said to the American sailor, "Why don't you *go?*"

As though he had not been trying his level best to go in the most dangerous ways imaginable! Now that his months of waiting were over, Jonathan Goble really did go—sailing back on Commodore Perry's flagship, and bringing into Japan the first Japanese Christian and the first Japanese Gospel of Matthew.

During the years of his living and working for God in the Land of the Rising Sun, Jonathan Goble's wife became very sick and could not walk at all. To help her get around town, he made her the first jinrikisha anybody had ever seen. She could sit back comfortably in this overgrown baby carriage and be whisked about as easily as you can say "taxi."

The Japanese were simply enchanted to see her whiz

past. "Make us another, honorable sir!" they begged. So he made another, and another, and another. Now everybody in the world connects a jinrickisha with Japan, but you and I will always think of Jonathan Goble, hurrying around to circulate the good news about Jesus Christ.

655 words

Chappie James: Patriot of the Skies

Judy Champion

Daniel James, Jr., was the youngest of seventeen children. His father was a hard worker and did all he could to provide for his family. He was employed as a street lamplighter in Pensacola, Florida, before electricity was introduced to the area of town where the blacks lived. From his father's example, Daniel learned not to be afraid of hard work.

Daniel's mother saw to the education of all of her children and several other neighborhood children. Mrs. James operated a small one-room schoolhouse in her home in which, as Daniel later recalled, "She taught us all the basics: love of God, love of country, and love of fellow man." The children also learned their numbers and how to read and write. Daniel proudly stated on many occasions that his mother was his "greatest inspiration."

Young Daniel had an older brother who was attending Florida A & M and playing football. Proud as only a younger brother can be, Daniel would seize every opportunity to extol his brother Chappie's football expertise. Eventually, it got to the point that all Daniel's friends ever heard was, Chappie this and Chappie that. Soon Daniel's pals had branded him also with the nickname Chappie, which ultimately replaced his real name.

Pensacola's skies were always teeming with aircraft from either the navy air station in town or Eglin Air Force Base a few miles to the east. Young Chappie James would crane his neck backward and search the sky for the plane or planes he could hear buzzing overhead. From earliest memories Chappie remembered how he yearned to fly.

After completing his first seven years of schooling under his mother's watchful eye, Chappie enrolled in a local public high school. Upon high school graduation in 1937, he entered the prestigious black college, Tuskegee Institute. There he earned a bachelor's degree and enlisted in the Air Corps Cadet program at the outbreak of World War II. Even though Chappie never fought during World War II, his career was underway, as he trained pilots for the first all-black squadron, the 99th.

Chappie James's first combat missions were flown during the Korean War. In a six-month tour of duty he flew 101 missions as a fighter pilot, earning the nickname "Black Panther" because of his skill and courage. Later when asked if his nickname was linked to the Black Panthers, a militant group of the sixties and seventies who led armed rebellions, Chappie replied, "I'm a different breed of cat. This Black Panther fights *for* his country."

During one flight over Korea, Chappie was shot down by the enemy. Fortunately for him a group of Marines were nearby when Chappie parachuted. They rescued him and safely delivered him back to his base only to watch Chappie climb into another plane and return to action.

In the spring of 1956, Chappie had distinguished himself as an expert fighter pilot and was promoted to lieutenant colonel.

Following an assignment in England, Chappie was transferred to Arizona and then to Thailand during the Vietnam War. A full colonel now, Chappie joined with another fighter named Robin Olds to become one of the most feared duos in the skies over North Vietnam. Together this respected fighter team was affectionately nicknamed "Black Man and Robin" by their comrades. On January 2, 1967, they knocked seven enemy planes out of the air; this represented the largest single air victory in the Vietnam War.

After his tour of duty in Vietnam during which he flew seventy-eight combat missions, Chappie was reassigned to Eglin Air Force Base in northwest Florida near his hometown of Pensacola. Even though Chappie James had become an important military figure, he never forgot his family and friends back home. One of Chappie's friends recalls that every time Chappie would fly home during the 1940s and 1950s, he would make a low pass over his old neighborhood with his jet to signal his arrival. Immediately his friends or family would drive out to the base to pick him up and bring him home.

Colonel James was always involved in another fight, besides the country's battles. He gave endlessly of himself to try to better racial relations within the service and civilian life. As Chappie once said, "I just might be an inspiration to that kid on the ghetto sidewalk to pick up a degree instead of a brick." He wanted racial barriers broken down, but in a peaceful, lawful manner. His motto was "Build a nation, not tear it down." He always tried to remember his mother's advice that he shouldn't be part of the problem but always contribute to the solution.

After a brief stay in Florida, Chappie was given command of Wheelus Air

Force Base in Libya. This was during a tension-filled time in the United States and Libyan relationship. Chappie's presence was a stabilizing force.

When Chappie was reassigned to the Pentagon after Libya, he was commissioned as a brigadier general. He was the second black man in United States history to receive this rank. He was named deputy assistant secretary of defense, and his main job was speaking on behalf of the armed services all over the country. This was during the height of anti-Vietnam sentiment and anti-America sentiment by some blacks, making Chappie's job a difficult one. The first time he spoke on a college campus he was hit by snowballs and later spit upon for his patriotic speeches. As Chappie James proudly erected his full 6'4", 230-pound frame, he unashamedly announced, "This is my country, and I believe in her, and I believe in her flag, and I'll defend her and I'll fight for her and serve her. If she has any ills, I'll stand by her and hold her hand until in God's given time, through her wisdom and her consideration for the welfare of the entire nation, things are made right again."

Chappie's last assignment was commander-in-chief of NORAD (North American Air Defense Command) in Colorado Springs, Colorado. He had now earned the highest rank of any black serviceman, a four-star general in the United States Air Force.

Chappie retired from active duty in the Air Force on February 1 and suffered a massive heart attack a few weeks later. He died on February 25, 1978, at the age of 58. Daniel "Chappie" James was a true patriot. He was, it has been said, a born leader who led well because he had compassion for people. Over 7,000 people, including many dignitaries, attended the two services for Chappie James. As one friend said, "No wonder his heart only lasted 58 years, he used it so much."

STOP 1,005 words

The Man with Two Lives

Elizabeth Rider Montgomery

Alice's Adventures in Wonderland—what a throng of pleasant memories that title brings to mind! The Cheshire Cat that disappeared, leaving its grin behind it. The Mad Hatter and his tea party. The Duchess who was always finding morals in things. Anyone who did not read *Alice's Adventures in Wonderland* during childhood missed a great pleasure, and still has a treat in store. It is a classic that will never grow old.

Did you ever wonder what sort of person wrote about Alice's adventures? Do you picture Lewis Carroll as an irresponsible, prank-playing, undignified person? Do you feel that only a very nonsensical man could write such delightful nonsense?

Then you are wrong. Quite wrong. For the author of this book of pure fun was a staid and dignified university professor of mathematics. Not only that, he wrote learned textbooks on mathematics. And to cap the climax, he was also a clergyman and a bachelor!

Charles Lutwidge Dodgson had been a lecturer on mathematics at Oxford University for more than ten years. He had even (as was expected of all professors of his rank) studied for the ministry and had become a clergyman of the Church of England. But he did not preach often. He was a very shy man. Adults almost frightened him. Then, too, he sometimes stammered badly, which made preaching difficult.

No, Dodgson did not make friends easily with men and women. But with children it was different. With children he felt at ease and happy, not shy and self-conscious. He made friends readily with every child he met. Although he had no children of his own, he understood young people very well indeed.

Three of his child friends were the three little daughters of Dean Liddell, the dean of the college where he taught. He loved to play games with them, to tell them stories, to make up nonsense verses. And the Liddell girls thought that the Reverend Charles Lutwidge Dodgson was the best playmate that ever was.

One summer afternoon Charles Dodgson was taking the Liddell girls for a boat ride on the Isis River. The day was hot, the river very quiet and peaceful. Nothing exciting happened, and the girls began to be restless.

Suddenly Alice said, "Tell us a story, won't you, please?"

Charles Dodgson rested on his oars and looked at the little girl with a twinkle in his eye.

"Why, yes," he said after a moment. "I'll tell you a story about a little girl named Alice, who became very bored and restless one afternoon—"

And he went right on with the story. While Alice of the story was wondering what her sister could find interesting in a book that had no pictures, a rabbit came hurrying past, talking to himself.

The girls listened enraptured as Alice fell down the deep, deep hole, and as she met the Cheshire Cat who had such an annoying habit of disappearing without warning.

Finally the Reverend Dodgson stopped for breath. "Now let's wait till next time for the rest."

The three girls sat very still in the bottom of the boat for almost a minute. Then Edith said, "It's next time now. Go ahead."

Dodgson laughed. But he went ahead.

Again he stopped for breath and said, "Let's leave the rest till next time."

In a minute Alice said, "Now it's next time. Go ahead. Please go ahead!"

So he went on with the story. Almost the whole of *Alice's Adventures in Wonderland* he told to the three little girls that afternoon in the

73

boat and on the bank of the river where they stopped to picnic.

When at last he took the children home, they begged him to write it down.

"I want it for my very own," said Alice. "So I can hear it over and over. It's my story, you know, because she has my very same name."

"And you'll make pictures too, won't you?" begged Edith. "Funny pictures, you know, like you often make for us."

Dodgson promised.

And he kept his promise. He wrote out the story, which at the time he called *Alice Underground* adding the nonsense rhymes and amusing pictures, and gave it to Alice, because it was her very own story. And how the girls and their friends enjoyed it!

But Dodgson never thought of having it published until George Macdonald, who was the author of *At the Back of the North Wind,* happened to see it.

"You must have it published," he urged Dodgson. "It's wrong to keep all that fun from other children. That book belongs to childhood—to all children everywhere."

Now, as you know, Dodgson loved children, although he had none of his own. So he decided he would have it published if what his friend

Macdonald said was true. He engaged an artist, Sir John Tenniel, to draw the pictures for it, because he felt his own sketches weren't good enough.

And of course he had to have a pen name. He couldn't think of publishing a ridiculous, rollicking story for children under the name of Charles Lutwidge Dodgson, mathematics professor and clergyman of the Church of England. Why, that name was widely known in educational circles as that of the author of such books as *A Syllabus of Plane Algebraic Geometry* and *The Formulae of Plane Trigonometry*. Undoubtedly he must use a pen name.

Fortunately he had one ready. A few years before he had begun sending verses and stories to a London comic weekly. At that time he had worked out a name from the Latin version of his two first names, Lutwidge and Charles. The name came out Lewis Carroll.

So it was that, under the name of Lewis Carroll, *Alice's Adventures in Wonderland* was published and became famous. Eventually, as Lewis Carroll, he wrote other books of the same type, as well as several more mathematics textbooks under his own name, always keeping his two names and his two lives widely separated.

Charles Dodgson would never admit to anyone but his children friends that he was the author of their favorite books. And he didn't need to admit it to them. They knew it without being told. They knew that no one but their friend could write such wonderful books.

STOP 1,050 words

Cartier the Explorer

Note these words:
Jacques (zhäk)
Cartier (kär·tyā′)
succulent: *juicy*
Gaspé (găs·pā′)
Chaleur (shə·lōōr′)

Excitement stirred the little French seaport of St. Malo on a beautiful May morning in 1534. Townspeople clustered on the docks, their eyes fixed expectantly on two great vessels that lay beside the ancient wharves. High on the deck of one of the ships Jacques Cartier watched the last man come aboard and then gave the order to sail.

Amid the cries of seagulls overhead, the flutter of waving arms and shouted farewells, came the shrill command "Cast off!" Slowly the ships pulled away from the dock and headed for the open sea.

Cartier was a sea-dog, a rugged sailor who loved the sea deeply and in whose dark eyes gleamed the spirit of adventure. He had already visited America. Now he was off in the service of Francis I, the clever King of France who entertained ambitions in the New World. Cartier was going to the strange new continent that lay across the route to the East, and before long he would be exploring the Grand Bank fisheries and moving into the very heart of the new-found-land.

For many weeks they listened to the wash of waves over the bows, the sigh of wind in the rigging, before they heard the cry "Land ho!" But there was little excitement on board, for Newfoundland was a place already well known to French sailors and fishermen. Round the north of the big island they sailed, down the Strait of Belle Isle in sight of the rugged shores of Labrador, and finally into the Gulf of St. Lawrence. It was late June by this time; the weather was mild and pleasant. The crew were delighted with the lush foliage of the shores, prickly gooseberries, succulent raspberries and strawberries. Southward they went to Prince Edward Island, and turning northward, coasted along the shores of New Brunswick to Gaspé. By the time they had reached the wide bay that lies between New Brunswick and Gaspé, the weather had become so warm they named the bay *Chaleur,* the French word for heat.

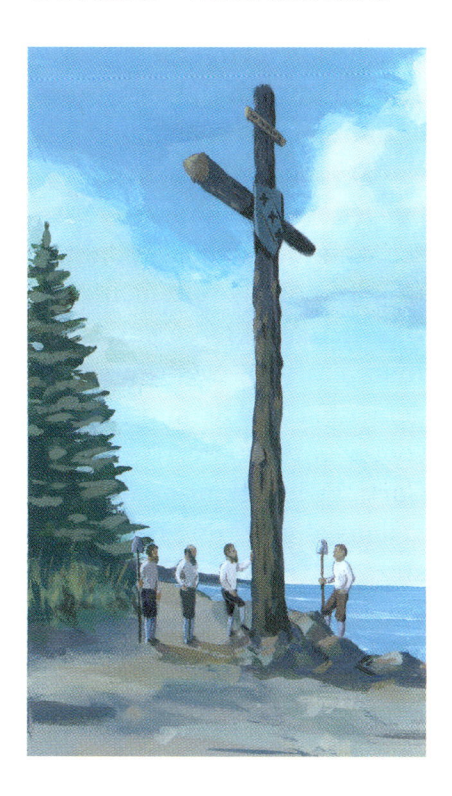

The seamen went ashore on Gaspé and set about the task of claiming the land for the King of France. They erected a heavy wooden cross thirty feet high, on which was placed a crest bearing lilies of France, and above that a piece of wood with the words "Long live the King of France." When this labor was completed they held a ceremony in which they formally declared possession of the land and asked God's blessing. A band of Indians nearby watched curiously, wondering at the strange actions of the white-faced men from the big ships.

During the summer Cartier made a complete circuit of the Gulf of St. Lawrence, but, strangely enough, missed the broad entrance to the river itself.

The following year Cartier was back in America with three ships and enough stores to keep his men for a winter. This time, with the assistance of Indian guides, he found the St. Lawrence River and pushed up its course, eager to see where the waters might lead him. His excitement was increased by remarkable Indian tales of wealthy kingdoms that lay along the shores of the great river. Into Cartier's imagination flowed visions of gleaming cities, stores of treasures, and empires as amazing as those of Mexico and Peru.

Through the soft days of early autumn they moved up the river, eyes scanning the shores for shining towers and battlements. Upon arriving at the first Indian Kingdom, Cartier's bright hopes were crushed at a glance: there was no great city, no fabulous wealth. To the eyes of the Frenchman there was only a sprawling, dirty, crude village. He was bitterly disappointed.

Leaving the two larger ships, he took the smallest vessel and proceeded farther up the river to the second Indian village, where Montreal now stands. He climbed the high hill near the village and stood enthralled by the magnificent landscape that spread away before him—the glorious sweep of the river, the white rapids and the distant purple of the hills. The view was magnificent in all its autumn splendour. In admiration Cartier named the place Mount Royal.

After taking leave of the friendly Indians of the district, the French returned to the first village and made preparation for the winter. Cartier ordered the vessels hauled up on shore, and a fort built for winter accommodation.

Snows came and the river froze over. The days became colder and colder—to the utter bewilderment of the French, who had never known such cruel temperatures. They began to realize how badly prepared they were for such severe conditions, and thought gloomily of the long months ahead. The fort was not warm; their clothing was not heavy enough; the food was largely salted meat.

Then came the dread menace of scurvy, the wasting disease that sickened and killed. One by one the men were stricken. Jacques Cartier looked with compassion on the pale faces and swollen bodies. The long days dragged on in monotonous succession, with more men falling sick and already twenty-five dead. "We'll all die before spring unless a miracle happens!" muttered the worried leader.

The miracle happened when a friendly Indian told them of an old remedy, a brew made from the bark of the white spruce. Cartier lost no time in testing the medicine, and was overjoyed with the results. Later he wrote in his journal that during the next six days his men used up the bark from a spruce that was as big as any oak in France. The brew was effective immediately, and the men were soon restored to health.

Further worries, however, were to trouble the sea captain. Suspecting the weakened condition of the French, the Indians became so openly hostile that Cartier feared they might launch a sudden attack. He ordered his men to move about and to make a noise by beating the walls with sticks and stones. This appeared to be successful, for no serious incident occurred.

Finally it was spring, and the St. Lawrence shone clear and blue beneath warm skies. With great joy the men prepared the ships for the homeward voyage to France.

Jacques Cartier did not find a passage through America to the East, nor did he find rich cities in the valley of the St. Lawrence, but he did reach the interior of Canada and gave us such honoured names as St. Lawrence, Mount Royal and Canada.

1,068 words

Reading Record and Quizzes

Reading Record

Selection	Words/Minute	Grade
Rocket Man: Wernher von Braun	_____	_____
Francis Scott Key's Banner	_____	_____
Mr. McGuffey and His Readers	_____	_____
"Keep Cool with Cal"	_____	_____
Isaac Newton: "The Great Ocean of Truth"	_____	_____
Man's Beginning	_____	_____
Dr. Livingstone, I Presume?	_____	_____
Mary Slessor: Queen of the Cannibals	_____	_____
Fact or Fiction? Aesop's Fables	_____	_____
Accidental Author, Part 1	_____	_____
Accidental Author, Part 2	_____	_____
The Book That Converted Its Author, Part 1	_____	_____
The Book That Converted Its Author, Part 2	_____	_____
Momentous Decision, Part 1	_____	_____
Momentous Decision, Part 2	_____	_____
He Used His Head, Part 1	_____	_____
He Used His Head, Part 2	_____	_____
He Used His Head, Part 3	_____	_____
Parable of Patriotism, Part 1	_____	_____
Parable of Patriotism, Part 2	_____	_____

Selection	Words/Minute	Grade
Inseparable Brothers, Part 1	_____	_____
Inseparable Brothers, Part 2	_____	_____
Johnny-Jump-Up, Part 1	_____	_____
Johnny-Jump-Up, Part 2	_____	_____
The Games Begin	_____	_____
Can Do. Will Do. Did!, Part 1	_____	_____
Can Do. Will Do. Did!, Part 2	_____	_____
Can Do. Will Do. Did!, Part 3	_____	_____
Chappie James: Patriot of the Skies	_____	_____
The Man with Two Lives	_____	_____
Cartier the Explorer	_____	_____

Name _____

Quiz 1
*Rocket Man:
Wernher von Braun*
Page 1

Directions: *Circle or write the correct answer.*

_____ %

_____ wpm

1. What kind of engineer was Wernher von Braun?
    a. astronautic
    b. aeronautic
    c. aquanautic

2. True or False: **Thrust** is the technical term for the "push" of a rocket.

3. True or False: Wernher von Braun grew up in London.

4. True or False: World War II was greatly influenced by Hitler's rocket corps.

5. True or False: Wernher von Braun's studies pointed him to God.

6. Wernher von Braun was in charge of the United States _?_ program.
    a. military
    b. citizenship
    c. space

Number of words: 350 ÷ _____ Minutes reading time = rate_____   85

Name _____

Quiz 2
Francis Scott Key's Banner
Page 3

Directions: *Circle or write the correct answer.*

_____ %

_____ wpm

1. What was Francis Scott Key's profession?
    a. musician
    (b.) lawyer
    c. soldier

2. (True) or False: Francis Scott Key wrote both the words and the music to "The Star-Spangled Banner."

3. ~~True~~ or (False) The original flag that flew over Fort McHenry can now be seen at the White House in Washington, D.C.

4. In what year was "The Star-Spangled Banner" adopted as America's official national anthem?

    1931

5. Near what city did the battle at Fort McHenry take place?

    Baltamor

6. According to the flag, how many states must have been part of the United States at the time of the War of 1812?
    (a.) 15
    b. 30
    c. 50

Number of words: 365 ÷ ____ Minutes reading time = rate ____   87

Quiz 3
Mr. McGuffey and His Reader
Page 5

Name _____

_____ %

_____ wpm

Directions: *Circle or write the correct answer.*

1. In the early 1800s, what section of the United States was "the new frontier"?
    a. the West
    b. the Midwest
    c. the South

2. True or False: Evidently Mr. McGuffey did not believe that schoolbooks should teach children about God.

3. True or False: McGuffey's readers had a great influence on the children of America and even children in some foreign countries.

4. What was Mr. McGuffey's profession?
    a. educator
    b. minister
    c. both **a** and **b**

5. When were the McGuffey readers first published?

   _____

6. True or False: McGuffey's readers are still in print today.

Number of words: 370 ÷ _____ Minutes reading time = rate_____

Name _____

Quiz 4
"Keep Cool with Cal"
Page 7

Directions: *Circle or write the correct answer.*

_____ %

_____ wpm

1. Calvin Coolidge was Vice President under what President?
    a. Harry Truman
    b. Warren Harding
    c. Grover Cleveland

2. True or False: Coolidge was America's 30th President.

3. What was Coolidge's nickname?
    a. "Cool Cal"
    b. "Silent Cal"

4. True or False: President Coolidge credited the success of his political ideas to his father.

5. True or False: As President, Coolidge believed that making more laws would help Americans.

6. True or False: Calvin Coolidge's Christian principles influenced his beliefs about America's needs.

Number of words: 380 ÷ _____ Minutes reading time = rate _____

Name _____

Quiz 7
Dr. Livingstone, I Presume?
Page 13

Directions: *Circle or write the correct answer.*

_____ %

_____ wpm

1. When Doctor Livingstone first went to Africa, he worked with what other great missionary?
    a. Mary Slessor
    b. Robert Moffat
    c. Henry Stanley

2. David Livingstone was a doctor and a missionary who was also one of the world's most famous ? .
   _____.

3. David Livingstone traced the course of which African river?
    a. Zambezi   b. Nile   c. Congo

4. Livingstone became the first European to see Africa's largest waterfall. He named the falls after which Queen?
   _____

5. Who said, "Dr. Livingstone, I presume?"
   _____

6. True or False: The newspaperman who found Dr. Livingstone stayed to help explore Africa.

7. What was David Livingstone doing at the time of his death?
    a. praying   b. preaching   c. exploring

8. True or False: The Africans appreciated David Livingstone for what he did, but they never came to love him.

9. Why did the Africans bury Dr. Livingstone's heart in Africa?
    a. They were members of a savage tribe.
    b. They wanted to preserve Dr. Livingstone's memory.
    c. They were complying with Dr. Livingstone's last wishes.

10. Why did the British bury Dr. Livingstone's body in Westminster Abbey?
    a. to honor him
    b. to please his African friends
    c. to comply with his last wishes

Number of words: 510 ÷ _____ Minutes reading time = rate_____   97

Name _____

Quiz 8
*Mary Slessor:
Queen of the
Cannibals*
Page 15

Directions: *Circle or write the correct answer.*

_____ %

_____ wpm

1. In what country was Mary Slessor born?
   a. Scotland   **b.** England   **c.** Ireland

2. Mary went to Africa to work in the area that is known by what name today?
   a. Algeria   **b.** Nigeria   **c.** Niger

3. What was the Africans' name for Mary?

   _____

4. For how many years was Mary a missionary in Africa?
   a. 10 years   **b.** 20 years   **c.** 40 years

5. Which of these facts about Mary Slessor is *not* true?
   a. Mary built houses and churches with her own hands.
   b. She taught people to read.
   c. She reared thousands of African children.
   d. She brought Christ to thousands.

6. What happened to Mary that made her unfortunate childhood bearable?

   _____

7. True or False: When Mary was the age of some sixth graders, she was already working to support her family.

8. True or False: The Africans considered twin babies to be a sign of their god's blessing.

9. True or False: Africa became more civilized because of Mary Slessor's influence.

Number of words: 575 ÷ _____ Minutes reading time = rate_____   99

Name _____

Quiz 9
Fact or Fiction?
Aesop's Fables
Page 17

Directions: *Circle or write the correct answer.*

_____ %

_____ wpm

1. True or False: Aesop often provided entertainment at banquets.

2. True or False: Aesop lived before the time of Christ.

3. Which of these facts about Aesop is *not* true?
    a. He had a sense of humor.
    b. He became famous.
    c. He disliked public speaking.

4. True or False: This article never mentions where Aesop may have lived.

5. Yes or No: Could some of Aesop's fables have been older than Aesop?

6. Which of these fables is *not* mentioned in some way in this selection?
    a. The Hare and the Tortoise
    b. The Wolf and the Lamb
    c. The Goose That Laid the Golden Eggs

7. True or False: It is said that Aesop's master gave him his freedom as a reward for his wit and wisdom.

8. True or False: This article shows that you have to be beautiful to be admired.

Number of words: 590 ÷ _____ Minutes reading time = rate_____ 101

Name _____

Quiz 10
Accidental Author
Part 1
Page 19

Directions: *Circle or write the correct answer.*

_____ %

_____ wpm

1. What author is this article about?
    a. J. A. Turner
    b. Captain Howell
    c. Joel Chandler Harris

2. After 1876, in what city did this author live?

   _____

3. What had this man been doing since he was fourteen years old?
    a. working for a newspaper
    b. writing stories
    c. working on a plantation

4. How did this author happen to begin writing a newspaper column?
    a. He replaced a man who had quit.
    b. He replaced a man who had been fired.
    c. He applied for the job.

5. What famous character did he create?
    a. Peter Rabbit   b. Bambi   c. Br'er Rabbit

6. Uncle Remus was probably patterned after a real story-teller called _?_ .
    a. Uncle Si   b. Uncle George   c. Captain Howell

7. True or False: Evidently this author was a young man before the Civil War.

8. What did the article *not* say about this author?
    a. He was red-headed.
    b. He was shy.
    c. He was a widower.

Number of words: 600 ÷ ____ Minutes reading time = rate____   103

Name _____

Quiz 11
Accidental Author
Part 2
Page 21

Directions: *Circle or write the correct answer.*

_____ %

_____ wpm

1. What name did Joel Chandler Harris give to the old man in his stories?

   _____

2. True or False: Mr. Harris contacted a publishing firm to inquire about putting his stories in a book.

3. Altogether, Mr. Harris wrote ? books of animal stories.
   - **a.** 5
   - **b.** 4
   - **c.** 3

4. Mr. Harris wrote his stories for ? .
   - **a.** *Lippincott's Magazine*
   - **b.** the *Atlanta Constitution*

5. Mr. Harris's first book was entitled, *Uncle Remus, His* _____ *and His Sayings*.

6. When his first book proved to be a success, Mr. Harris was ? .
   - **a.** amazed
   - **b.** not surprised
   - **c.** irritated by the publicity

7. Joel Chandler Harris's attitude toward his abilities could be described as ? .
   - **a.** humble
   - **b.** proud
   - **c.** uncaring

8. True or False: It was Joel Chandler Harris's lifetime dream to become a writer.

Number of words: 465 ÷ ____ Minutes reading time = rate____ 105

Name _____

Quiz 12
The Book That Converted Its Author Part 1
Page 23

_____ %

_____ wpm

Directions: *Circle or write the correct answer.*

1. The author Lew Wallace had several vocations, *not* including the __?__.
    a. law   **b.** military   **c.** church

2. Why did he begin writing *Ben Hur*?
    a. to learn the truth about Jesus
    b. to relieve his boredom after the excitement of the war
    c. to earn some money

3. In what war had Wallace been a soldier?
    a. War of 1812
    b. Civil War
    c. Spanish-American War

4. True or False: Wallace first began studying the Bible to learn about the Wise Men.

5. Another name for "Wise Men" given in this selection is __?__.
    a. Magi   **b.** Bethlehemites   **c.** neither of these

6. From the introductory remarks, what did you *not* learn about the book *Ben-Hur*?
    a. Ben-Hur is the name of the hero.
    b. Ben-Hur is the winner of an exciting chariot race.
    c. The story takes place during the time of Christ.

7. What did Wallace decide that he should do to learn about what to believe?
    a. study theology
    b. read sermons
    c. read the Bible

8. What prompted Wallace's regret that he was so ignorant about religion?
    a. the war
    b. a discussion at a friend's home
    c. a book

Number of words: 635 ÷ ____ Minutes reading time = rate____   107

Quiz 13

The Book That Converted Its Author Part 2
Page 25

Name _____

Directions: *Circle or write the correct answer.*

_____ %

_____ wpm

1. True or False: Evidently Wallace had already written a book which he had entitled *The Fair God*.

2. How long did Lew Wallace work on *Ben-Hur?*
    a. approximately 7 weeks
    b. approximately 7 months
    c. approximately 7 years

3. Lew Wallace began *Ben-Hur* with the story of the Wise Men and ended it with the ? .
    a. crucifixion
    b. resurrection
    c. ascension

4. Which of these is *not* a reason for the long time it took him to write the book?
    a. It required much research.
    b. Wallace's wife objected to his work.
    c. Wallace could work on the book only in his spare time.

5. In 1878, Wallace was made governor of what territory?
    a. Arizona   b. New Mexico   c. Colorado

6. True or False: At one point, Wallace's life was threatened by Jesse James.

7. True or False: *Ben-Hur* became popular immediately.

8. Wallace "took infinite pains to verify every fact, to substantiate every statement." This shows that he was ? .
    a. careless   b. diligent   c. neglectful

9. Which of the books Wallace wrote led to his becoming a Christian?
    a. *The Fair God*   b. *Ben-Hur*

Number of words: 565 ÷ ____ Minutes reading time = rate ____   109

Name _____

Quiz 14
Momentous Decision Part 1
Page 28

Directions: *Circle or write the correct answer.*

_____ %

_____ wpm

1. Which short-story character is an invention of Washington Irving?
    a. Ali Baba
    b. Ichabod Crane
    c. Pecos Bill

2. This period of Washington Irving's life occurred at what time?
    a. early 1800s   b. mid-1800s   c. late 1800s

3. Washington went to what city to help out in his family's mercantile business?
    a. London   b. Birmingham   c. Liverpool

4. True or False: Washington became bored with the mercantile business and soon quit.

5. We are introduced to Washington Irving as he is __?__.
    a. brooding about his failures
    b. fighting with his sister
    c. thinking about his future

6. Which of the following men is *not* mentioned as being a brother of Washington Irving?
    a. Peter   b. William   c. Decatur   d. Ebenezer

7. True or False: Washington Irving was forced to become a writer because there were no other positions available for him.

8. Which of the following phrases does *not* describe Washington Irving?
    a. the first American writer to receive recognition abroad
    b. the first American writer to achieve real success in America
    c. the middle son in his family

9. How did Washington Irving's sister feel about his becoming a writer?
    a. She thought he would not make any money.
    b. She thought he would soon change his mind.
    c. She thought her husband would disapprove.

Number of words: 650 ÷ _____ Minutes reading time = rate_____   111

Quiz 15

Name _____

Momentous Decision Part 2
Page 30

_____ %

_____ wpm

Directions: *Circle or write the correct answer.*

1. True or False: Washington Irving's brothers were disappointed by his decision to make a career in literature.

2. Give the name of a well-known story included as one of the first parts in Irving's *The Sketch Book*.

   _____

3. The people in Tarrytown, New York, were evidently of what origin?
   a. English   **b.** Hessian   **c.** Dutch

4. What character, introduced to Irving by his brother-in-law, prompted him to write "The Legend of Sleepy Hollow"?
   a. Hendrick Hudson
   b. Brom Bones
   c. Hal Van Wart

5. After Irving decided to write, he chose to write about American legends and the country of _?_.

   _____

6. True or False: Washington Irving had already written one book entitled *Knickerbocker History of New York*.

7. How long did it take Irving to prove that he could earn a living by writing?
   a. 1 year   **b.** 5 years   **c.** 10 years

8. True or False: Washington Irving's stories were read and loved all over Germany as well as America.

9. True or False: Before Washington Irving, there were no American writers that the world admired.

Number of words: 610 ÷ _____ Minutes reading time = rate _____   113

Name _____

Quiz 16
He Used His Head
Part 1
Page 32

Directions: *Circle or write the correct answer.*

_____ %

_____ wpm

1. What great man is this story about?

   _____

2. What famous explorer did he enjoy pretending to be when he was a young boy?
    - **a.** Captain Hook
    - **b.** Captain Cook
    - **c.** Captain Long John Silver

3. In what country was Bill born?
    - **a.** Germany
    - **b.** France
    - **c.** England

4. True or False: Bill showed a remarkable talent for painting from the very beginning.

5. When Bill was fourteen, he had to begin making his own living. What work did he do?
    - **a.** made shoes
    - **b.** made barrels
    - **c.** wove cloth

6. What did he hang over his workbench?

   _____

7. True or False: He taught himself six languages as he worked.

8. True or False: The people in his church were enthusiastic about sending him to a foreign country.

9. True or False: English would be considered a "dead" language.

Number of words: 590 ÷ _____ Minutes reading time = rate_____   115

Name _____

Quiz 17
He Used His Head
Part 2
Page 34

Directions: *Circle or write the correct answer.*

_____ %

_____ wpm

1. True or False: William Carey got people aroused about missions by writing letters to the editors of newspapers.

2. The people in William's church voted to send him to what country as a missionary?

_____

3. What was the first language that William had to learn?
    a. Bengali
    b. Hindu
    c. Indian

4. How many different tongues did William learn to speak?
    a. 12
    b. 22
    c. 32

5. True or False: Most of the money for William Carey's endeavors was given to him by other people.

6. William built a school for _?_.
    a. lepers
    b. orphans
    c. Hindus

7. William built a hospital for _?_.
    a. lepers
    b. orphans
    c. Hindus

8. Which statement best expresses William's attitude toward each task before him?
    a. If I have enough money, I can do it.
    b. If I have enough time, I can do it.
    c. If God helps me, I can do it.

Number of words: 660 ÷ ____ Minutes reading time = rate____ 117

Name _____

Quiz 18
*He Used His Head
Part 3
Page 36*

Directions: *Circle or write the correct answer.*

_____ %

_____ wpm

1. The streets in Calcutta were ugly, so what did William do?
   a. cleaned them
   b. put out litter bins
   c. planted flowers

2. Which of the following statements about William Carey is *not* true.
   a. He treated sick people.
   b. He made the most famous gardens in the entire Orient.
   c. He sent to England for men to come teach the people in India how to farm.

3. True or False: William Carey could accurately be called a problem solver.

4. Half of the Indians' problems were due to poor _____.

5. How many years did William Carey labor in India before anyone accepted Christ?

   _____

6. What religion did the Indian people follow?
   a. Catholicism   b. Islam   c. Hinduism

7. Evidently the word "botanical" refers to _?_ .
   a. animals   b. plants   c. medicines

8. True or False: Krishna Pal was the only Indian who became a Christian.

Number of words: 515 ÷ _____ Minutes reading time = rate _____   119

Name _____

Quiz 19

Parable of
Patriotism:
The Man without
a Country Part 1
Page 38

Directions: *Circle or write the correct answer.*

_____ %

_____ wpm

1. What career did Edward Everett Hale want for his life's work?

   _____

2. True or False: During the Civil War, Hale was on the side of the Union.

3. Hale encouraged people during the Civil War by writing morale-building articles in what magazine?
   a. *Saturday Evening Post*
   b. *Atlantic Monthly*
   c. The name of the magazine was not given in the article.

4. Who was the President of the United States during the Civil War? _____

5. In the early days of the war, which side appeared to be losing?
   a. the North   **b.** the South

6. Hale got the idea for his story from a statement made by ? .
   a. Fields   **b.** Burnside   **c.** Vallandigham

7. From reading this article, we know that the Civil War occurred ? .
   a. during the 1760s
   b. during the 1860s
   c. during the 1960s

8. True or False: Mr. Hale's story decreased patriotic feelings.

9. What is the best thing that could be accomplished by sending away the politician who said he did not want to belong to his country?
   a. rid the nation of dissenting opinions
   b. make the man suffer for expressing his beliefs
   c. make the man realize what it is like to be without his country and repent his words

Number of words: 705 ÷ ____ Minutes reading time = rate____   121

Name _____

Quiz 20

Parable of Patriotism: The Man without a Country Part 2

Page 41

Directions: *Circle or write the correct answer.*

_____ %

_____ wpm

1. True or False: Before Mr. Hale wrote his story, he prepared by reading about American traitors.

2. What did Mr. Hale name the character in his story?
    a. Aaron Burr
    b. Philip Nolan
    c. General Wilkinson

3. Vallandigham, the real-life man who had scorned his own country, was nominated for governor of what state?
    a. Iowa   b. Ohio   c. Illinois

4. Vallandigham was defeated because _?_ .
    a. Mr. Hale's story raised a public furor about him
    b. his name was removed from the ballot
    c. patriotic citizens did not vote for him

5. What is the full name of the author of "The Man without a Country"?

    _____

6. Mr. Hale lived in what city?
    a. Chicago   b. Richmond   c. Boston

7. Hale regretted that he was famous for his story. He would rather have been remembered as _?_ .
    a. an orator   b. a teacher   c. a preacher

8. Mr. Hale's story _?_ .
    a. strengthened the Union cause
    b. created sympathy for the South
    c. was printed too late to influence public opinion about the war

Number of words: 655 ÷ ____ Minutes reading time = rate____   123

Name _____

Quiz 21
Inseparable Brothers
Part 1
Page 44

Directions: *Circle or write the correct answer.*

_____ %

_____ wpm

1. What kind of stories do we associate with the Grimm brothers?
   _____

2. These stories were from what country? _____

3. The brothers wrote and collected their stories in the ? .
    a. early 1800s
    b. mid-1800s
    c. late 1800s

4. True or False: The two brothers earned their living working as librarians.

5. Which of these characteristics do *not* describe the two brothers?
    a. honest
    b. uneducated
    c. simple and unassuming

6. True or False: The literature of their country was passed down from one generation to another by word of mouth.

7. Why had the brothers vowed never to separate?
    a. They were orphans.
    b. They were extremely poor.
    c. This selection does not tell us.

8. The aim of the Grimm brothers was to ? .
    a. become famous writers
    b. become rich from their writing
    c. become the means by which ancient German literature was preserved

Number of words: 550 ÷ _____ Minutes reading time = rate_____   125

Quiz 22

Name _____

Inseparable Brothers Part 2
Page 46

Directions: *Circle or write the correct answer.*

_____ %

_____ wpm

1. True or False: In the beginning, the Grimm brothers made very slow progress in their efforts to find story sources.

2. True or False: The Grimms' most valuable resource was a man who was a direct descendant of one of Germany's great storytellers.

3. How many fairy tales did the brothers eventually gather?
       a. 100   **b.** 200   **c.** 300

4. The brothers collected the tales for _?_.
       a. adults   **b.** children

5. Which of these facts about the Grimm brothers is *not* true?
       a. They wrote scholarly works.
       b. They lived to be quite old.
       c. They published their first collection of stories in 1912.

6. How many books did the Grimms write?
       a. 10
       b. more than 10
       c. The selection does not tell us.

7. True or False: The brothers wrote a dictionary.

8. Which word best describes the Grimm brothers' attitudes toward their work?
       a. ponderous
       b. persistent
       c. pathetic

Number of words: 715 ÷ ____ Minutes reading time = rate_____

Name _____

Quiz 23
Johnny-Jump-Up
Part 1
Page 49

Directions: *Circle or write the correct answer.*

_____ %

_____ wpm

1. We can assume that Johnny ? .
    a. spent only his summers at the lumber camp
    b. lived year around at the lumber camp
    c. visited the lumber camp each winter

2. Which name was *not* given to a lumberjack in this selection?
    a. Hop Sing
    b. Slippy Sam
    c. Tuxedo Tex
    d. Hesitation Harry

3. What did Johnny do to create some excitement?
   _____

4. Why did Johnny have to stay in his room?
    a. He was recovering from an illness.
    b. He was hiding from the angry lumberjacks.
    c. He was being punished.

5. How did the men finally come to believe that Johnny was really telling the truth the second time?
    a. They saw the flames.
    b. Johnny looked serious this time.
    c. They smelled the smoke on his clothes.

6. The cook at the lumber camp was ? .
    a. Japanese   b. Chinese   c. Korean

7. What does this story teach?
    a. Boys are bad.
    b. Tricksters are not trusted.
    c. Lumberjacks are cruel.

Number of words: 865 ÷ _____ Minutes reading time = rate_____   129

Quiz 24

Johnny-Jump-Up
Part 2
Page 52

Name _____

_____ %

_____ wpm

Directions: *Circle or write the correct answer.*

1. True or False: The lumbermen reached the fire in time to put it out in just a few minutes.

2. What had Johnny's mother done at the lumber camp?

   _____

3. What Book did Tuxedo Tex inherit from his Aunt Amelia?

   _____

4. What man did Johnny "keep his eyes glued on" in the Book? _____

5. True or False: The lumberjacks had been using the name of Jesus as a curse word.

6. The main reason that Tuxedo gave the Book to Johnny to read was so that ? .
   a. he would have something to do
   b. he would learn not to lie
   c. he would learn how to read

7. What does this story teach?
   a. Reading the Bible can change people.
   b. Reading the Bible is hard for young people.
   c. Reading the Bible is just for women.

Number of words: 905 ÷ _____ Minutes reading time = rate_____   131

Quiz 25
The Games Begin!
Page 55

Name _____

_____ %

_____ wpm

Directions: *Circle or write the correct answer.*

1. Where were the 1912 Olympic Games held?
    a. Sweden
    b. Switzerland
    c. Russia

2. True or False: Jim Thorpe won every track event in the 1912 Olympics.

3. Jim's father had told him to be proud that he was an _?_.
    a. American
    b. Indian
    c. athlete

4. True or False: Jim's teammate Louis Tewanima won a silver medal.

5. How many events are there in a pentathlon? _____

6. Jim Thorpe received a _?_ medal for his pentathlon win.
    a. gold
    b. silver
    c. bronze

7. What *three* things did Jim Thorpe receive in addition to his medal? (Circle three answers.)
    a. a laurel wreath
    b. a bronzed javelin
    c. a life-sized bust of King Gustav
    d. a gold chalice shaped like a Viking ship

8. True or False: King Gustav of Sweden said that Jim Thorpe was the greatest athlete in the world.

Number of words: 920 ÷ _____ Minutes reading time = rate_____ 133

Name _____

Quiz 26
Can Do. Will Do. Did! Part 1
Page 59

Directions: *Circle or write the correct answer.*

1. This selection is about what man?

    _____

    _____ %

    _____ wpm

2. What country was he trying so hard to enter?
    a. China
    b. Japan
    c. Korea

3. True or False: His fellow sailors urged him to keep trying.

4. How many times did he try in this selection? _____

5. How did he attempt to get into the country?

    _____

6. Which of the following words best describes this man?
    a. determined
    b. discouraged
    c. disheartened

7. What would be done to Christians who did not stay out of this country?

    _____

8. The shores of this country were lined with "sentries." Which word best describes what "sentries" are?
    a. high walls
    b. guards
    c. protective trees

Number of words: 780 ÷ _____ Minutes reading time = rate _____   135

Quiz 27

Name _____

Can Do. Will Do. Did! Part 2
Page 62

_____ %

_____ wpm

Directions: *Circle or write the correct answer.*

1. How many times was Jonathan Goble returned to his ship by the Japanese sentries?

   _____

2. How did Jonathan attempt to get past the sentries the last time?

   _____

3. Which of the following statements is *not* true?
   a. Jonathan's fellow sailors admired his pluck.
   b. Jonathan's fellow sailors feared for his life.
   c. Jonathan's fellow sailors understood his desire to get into Japan.

4. True or False: Jonathan decided that God was not blessing his efforts because they were done in a secret and undercover way.

5. Jonathan's ship docked at what American port?
   a. Boston   b. New York   c. Savannah

6. True or False: Commodore Perry was sent by the U.S. government to end a war between America and Japan.

7. The ruler of Japan is called the __?__.
   a. King   b. Emperor   c. President

8. True or False: The people in Jonathan's church compared him to the Apostle Paul.

9. Japan was called a "hermit nation" because __?__.
   a. her people were warlike
   b. her people wanted to be isolated from others
   c. her people were poor

Number of words: 925 ÷ _____ *Minutes reading time = rate* _____   137

Quiz 28

Name _____

Can Do. Will Do. Did! Part 3
Page 65

Directions: *Circle or write the correct answer.*

_____ %

_____ wpm

1. Japanese officials came to call on Commodore Perry's ship on what day of the week?

   _____

2. What was the name of the song that the band played and the sailors sang?
   - **a.** "The Old Rugged Cross"
   - **b.** "Old Hundred"
   - **c.** "Old Faithful"

3. True or False: Commodore Perry left his ship and gave the President's letter to the Emperor in a quiet, unimpressive manner.

4. True or False: Jonathan was not able to leave the ship with Commodore Perry and meet the Emperor.

5. Which book of the Bible did the stowaway help Jonathan Goble translate into Japanese?
   - **a.** Matthew
   - **b.** Mark
   - **c.** Malachi

6. For whom did Jonathan Goble make the first jinrikisha?

   _____

7. Since the jinrikisha is compared to an overgrown baby carriage, what do you suppose provides the power for its movements?
   - **a.** horses
   - **b.** oxen
   - **c.** people

8. Japan is called the Land of the _____.

Number of words: 655 ÷ ____ Minutes reading time = rate ____   139

Name _____

Quiz 29
Chappie James:
Patriot of the Skies
Page 68

Directions: *Circle or write the correct answer.*

_____ %
_____ wpm

1. How many children were born into Chappie's family?
       a. 10 **b.** 15 **c.** 17

2. What was Chappie's dad's job? _____

3. What was Chappie's hometown?
       a. Jacksonville, Florida
       b. Pensacola, Florida
       c. Tallahassee, Florida

4. What was in Chappie's hometown that influenced his choice of careers?
       a. a college that had a flight school
       b. a factory that built airplanes
       c. an air station that trained naval pilots

5. Who was Chappie's first teacher? _____

6. Which war was *not* mentioned in this article?
       a. WWI **b.** Korean War **c.** Vietnam War

7. True or False: Chappie sympathized with war protesters.

8. Which words describe Chappie? (Select more than one.)
       a. patriotic   **c.** bitter
       b. compassionate **d.** uneducated

9. Which accomplishment was *not* achieved by Chappie James?
       a. longest military career
       b. largest single air victory in Vietnam
       c. highest military rank earned by a black man at that time

10. Chappie died in 1978 _?_ .
        a. in a plane crash
        b. of a heart attack
        c. at a war-protest gathering

Number of words: 1,005 ÷ _____ Minutes reading time = rate _____ 141

Name _____

Quiz 30
The Man with Two Lives
Page 72

Directions: *Circle or write the correct answer.*

_____ %

_____ wpm

1. Charles Lutwidge Dodgson was this man's real name. What was his pen name?

   _____

2. He was a professor of _?_.
   a. mathematics
   b. literature
   c. theology

3. True or False: Mr. Dodgson felt more at ease with children than he did with adults.

4. Where was Mr. Dodgson when he first invented the story of Alice?
   a. on a swing
   b. in a boat
   c. in a park

5. True or False: Dodgson wrote down the story later and even added pictures.

6. True or False: He did not consider publishing the story until his friend George Macdonald urged him to.

7. True or False: This was the first book that he had ever written.

8. Dodgson would probably have been a wonderful _?_.
   a. preacher
   b. politician
   c. parent

Number of words: 1,050 ÷ ____ Minutes reading time = rate____ 143

Name _____

Quiz 31
*Cartier
the Explorer*
Page 76

Directions: *Circle or write the correct answer.*

_____ %

_____ wpm

1. What country did Cartier explore?
   a. Mexico
   b. Canada
   c. France

2. What was Cartier's first name?
   a. Francis
   b. Lawrence
   c. Jacques

3. What country did Cartier represent when he sailed to America?

   _____

4. What does the name *Chaleur* mean?
   a. heat
   b. beautiful
   c. water

5. What was Cartier looking for when he sailed up the St. Lawrence River?
   a. wealthy kingdoms
   b. more rivers
   c. Indian villages

6. True or False: Cartier and his men were unprepared for the harsh winter they faced.

7. What finally cured the deadly disease of scurvy?
   a. a powder made from oak leaves
   b. a fresh supply of meat
   c. a brew made from white spruce bark

8. Yes or No: Did Cartier find a passage through America to the East?

Number of words: 1,068 ÷ _____ Minutes reading time = rate_____ 145

Quiz Answer Key

Quiz 1 *Rocket Man: Wernher von Braun*—p. 85
1. a
2. true
3. false
4. false
5. true
6. c

Quiz 2 *Francis Scott Key's Banner*—p. 87
1. b
2. false
3. false
4. 1931
5. Baltimore
6. a

Quiz 3 *Mr. McGuffey and His Readers*—p. 89
1. b
2. false
3. true
4. c
5. 1836
6. true

Quiz 4 *"Keep Cool with Cal"*—p. 91
1. b
2. true
3. b
4. false
5. false
6. true

Quiz 5 *Isaac Newton: "The Great Ocean of Truth"*—p. 93
1. England
2. false
3. b
4. a
5. false
6. true

Quiz 6 *Man's Beginning*—p. 95
1. evolution
2. the Bible
3. false
4. true
5. false
6. true
7. false
8. b
9. a

Quiz 7 *Dr. Livingstone, I Presume?*—p. 97
1. b
2. explorers
3. a
4. Victoria
5. Henry Stanley
6. true
7. a
8. false
9. b
10. a

Quiz 8 *Mary Slessor: Queen of the Cannibals*—p. 99
1. a
2. b
3. "White Ma"
4. c
5. c
6. She came to know Christ.
7. true
8. false
9. true

Quiz 9 *Fact or Fiction? Aesop's Fables*—p. 101
1. true
2. true
3. c
4. false
5. yes
6. a
7. true
8. false

Quiz 10 *Accidental Author, Part 1*—p. 103
1. c
2. Atlanta
3. a
4. a
5. c
6. b
7. true
8. c

Quiz 11 *Accidental Author, Part 2*—p. 105
1. Uncle Remus
2. false
3. 5
4. b
5. Songs
6. a
7. a
8. false

Quiz 12 *The Book That Converted Its Author, Part 1*—p. 107
1. c
2. a
3. b
4. true
5. a
6. b
7. c
8. b

Quiz 13 *The Book That Converted Its Author, Part 2*—p. 109
1. true
2. c
3. a
4. b
5. b
6. false
7. false
8. b
9. b

Quiz 14 *Momentous Decision, Part 1*—p. 111
1. b
2. a
3. c
4. false
5. c
6. c
7. false
8. c
9. a

Quiz 15 *Momentous Decision, Part 2*—p. 113
1. true
2. "Rip Van Winkle"
3. c
4. b
5. England
6. true
7. a
8. false
9. true

147

Quiz 16 *He Used His Head, Part 1*—p. 115
1. William Carey
2. b
3. c
4. false
5. a
6. a map of the world
7. true
8. false
9. false

Quiz 17 *He Used His Head, Part 2*—p. 117
1. true
2. India
3. a
4. c
5. false
6. b
7. a
8. c

Quiz 18 *He Used His Head, Part 3*—p. 119
1. c
2. c
3. true
4. food
5. 7
6. c
7. b
8. false

Quiz 19 *Parable of Patriotism, Part 1*—p. 121
1. being a minister
2. true
3. b
4. Abraham Lincoln
5. a
6. c
7. b
8. false
9. c

Quiz 20 *Parable of Patriotism, Part 2*—p. 123
1. true
2. b
3. b
4. c
5. Edward Everett Hale
6. c
7. c
8. a

Quiz 21 *Inseparable Brothers, Part 1*—p. 125
1. fairy tales
2. Germany
3. a
4. true
5. b
6. true
7. c
8. c

Quiz 22 *Inseparable Brothers, Part 2*—p. 127
1. true
2. false
3. b
4. a
5. c
6. c
7. true
8. b

Quiz 23 *Johnny-Jump-Up, Part 1*—p. 129
1. b
2. a
3. He yelled, "Fire!"
4. c
5. c
6. b
7. b

Quiz 24 *Johnny-Jump-Up, Part 2*—p. 131
1. false
2. She had been the cook.
3. a Bible
4. John the Baptist
5. true
6. b
7. a

Quiz 25 *The Games Begin!*—p. 133
1. a
2. false
3. b
4. true
5. five
6. a
7. a, c, d
8. true

Quiz 26 *Can Do. Will Do. Did!, Part 1*—p. 135
1. Jonathan Goble
2. b
3. false
4. two times
5. swimming
6. a
7. Their heads would be cut off.
8. b

Quiz 27 *Can Do. Will Do. Did!, Part 2*—p. 137
1. 3
2. in a barrel
3. c
4. true
5. a
6. false
7. b
8. true
9. b

Quiz 28 *Can Do. Will Do. Did!, Part 3*—p. 139
1. Sunday
2. b
3. false
4. true
5. a
6. his wife
7. c
8. Rising Sun

Quiz 29 *Chappie James: Patriot of the Skies*—p. 141
1. c
2. He was a lamplighter.
3. b
4. c
5. his mother
6. a
7. false
8. a, b
9. a
10. b

Quiz 30 *The Man with Two Lives*—p. 143
1. Lewis Carroll
2. a
3. true
4. b
5. true
6. true
7. false
8. c

Quiz 31 *Cartier the Explorer*—p. 145
1. b
2. c
3. France
4. a
5. a
6. true
7. c
8. no